FIGHT YOUR HEALTH INSURER AND WIN

Secrets of the Insurance Warrior

FIGHT YOUR HEALTH INSURER AND WIN

Secrets of the Insurance Warrior

Laurie Todd

Healthwise Publications
Kirkland, Washington

Fight Your Health Insurer and Win: Secrets of the Insurance Warrior

Published by
Healthwise Publications
Kirkland, Washington

Contact address:
P.O. Box 2045, Woodinville, WA 98072

Phone: 425-497-1858 / Fax: 425-820-5947

Or order from our secure website:
www.theinsurancewarrior.com

SAN 852-5714

Healthwise Publications may be purchased in bulk for education, business, or fundraising use. For information, please contact the publisher.

Library of Congress Control Number 2004012345

ISBN-13: 978-0-9791435-0-2
ISBN-10: 0-9791435-0-0

Printed in the United States of America.

10 9 8 7 6 5 4 3 2 1

Cover Design by Cathi Stevenson, Book Cover Express,
www.bookcoverexpress.com

For Lisa Janson, R.N.
loyal sister, caregiver, and friend

Contents

Prologue

- Have you been diagnosed with cancer or some other expensive disease or condition?

- Do you wonder how to find the best-qualified doctor to treat your disease/condition?

- Do you feel as if nobody is managing your case?

- Do you face financial ruin because your health insurer refuses to pay?

Then, this is the book for you.

In the olden days—before the advent of managed care in 1970—you could count on your doctor to manage your case, keeping abreast of the latest treatments for your disease/ condition and referring you to a specialist as necessary. He/ she also ran interference with the insurance company, making sure that you got the care you needed to maintain your health or save your life.

Just in case you haven't checked since 1970 . . . the delivery of medical care has changed. With the explosion of new drugs and treatments, your doctor would be hard-pressed to keep up with the cutting-edge information about your disease. He probably has plenty to do just keeping up with the flood of patients, paperwork, and new insurance-company directives coming over his desk.

Directives from the insurance company to the doctor? How could this be? Well, nowadays the doctor is often employed by—or contracted with—the insurance company. If your doctor works for the system, it could be very inconvenient for him to buck the system. No more check and balance on the health insurer. Some bean counter armed with a list of symptoms gets to decide what care you receive. What are you going to do?

When I was suddenly diagnosed with a particularly difficult, so-called rare cancer, I soon discovered that not only did my in-network doctors not know anything about my disease, but the insurer was not about to pay for any treatment. Cancer? No treatment? It happens every day.

When I went looking for books to help me find my way through this healthcare swamp, I found one book by a lawyer, and one by an insurance expert. I discovered useful nuggets in both books, but precious little to arm me for the Clash of the Titans which was to come.

I am not a lawyer, nor am I an insurance expert. As soon as the tsunami of cancer tore through my life, I was left with no money, no job, no advantages. Quite frankly, I had the most inadequate insurance coverage this side of the Rockies. However, I did have the most important qualities necessary to defeat a health insurer: a serious will to live, an aversion to injustice, and a talent for persuasive letter-writing. As soon as I realized that my health insurer was trying to kill me, I rose up on my hind legs and became a lion of courage.

And, as soon as I recovered from treatment for my "rare" cancer—treatment by the foremost expert on this cancer, I might add, paid for by my reluctant insurer—I began to help others win their insurance wars. As this book goes to press, I have coached sixteen "helpees" on how to make their insurers pay . . . we have always won. What I am is a strategy expert and coach. I specialize in helping people to write appeals which get accepted.

I wrote this book in order to show you how to face off against your health insurer and to get the lifesaving treatment that you deserve. I will give you the grand strategy, the tactics, the language that you will need to win your own Clash of the Titans.

I have walked in your shoes—I fought my health insurer all alone while also fighting my cancer. My battle involved a tremendous amount of research, intellectual heavy-lifting, and reinventing of the wheel.

With this book, the fight will be much easier for you.

CHAPTER 1

Drafted:

How I Became the Insurance Warrior

I had a magic bullet to protect me forever from Bad Medical Trouble . . . my grandmother and all of her seven brothers and sisters lived to be over a hundred years old. In their last decades, these hearty souls were out fishing, gardening and canning tomatoes. Like all people in the Land of the Living, I found good reason to feel blessed, protected and safe.

And then, one day, I was felled like a giant redwood. Geezered overnight, I learned that cancer is no respecter of heartiness. Unbeknownst to me, I had been drafted into the Army of the Seriously Afflicted.

In order to get to boot camp, I had to tumble down a dizzying rabbithole and land with a great thud at Camp Cancer. When you enter Camp Cancer, you leave all logic behind. Everything is ironic—you are empowered by becoming a victim, you must open your heart to win a fierce battle and, in the process of letting go of hope, you may find peace. Just when doctors are quoting odds for your survival, you finally learn how not to be attached to outcomes. The people who control your new world—doctors, nurses and insurance company bureaucrats—may say things which defy logic, insult your intelligence, or just plain boggle the mind. I had to embark upon a letter-writing campaign in order to find out the truth about my condition; I had to search the entire United States to find a doctor who treated me as an equal. Since my draft notice into this army was a Stage IV cancer, my basic training had to be short, very short. I learned how to mastermind my own treatment, how to trust my own judgment and how to call for support. The cavalry galloped in—in the form of family, friends and colleagues. New friends appeared who steered me in the right direction. Over time, I was privileged to encounter selfless dedication, help with no conditions, and dazzling feats of compassion.

I came to the first few awful bad-news doctor appointments like a tender recruit. Weeks to live, months to live, 30% chance of five years to live, two good years left. It was the "two good years" that burst my bubble of civilian innocence. Two years? In that moment, I rose up on my hind legs and started questioning my doctors. How come? Says who? Based on what? From that moment on, I started to perfect my strategy and to take charge of my own survival.

Thankfully, people can change. In Camp Cancer, they shape up at lightning speed. Within three months, I had grown from a shell-shocked victim to a feisty, crusty, shameless, blameless old soldier who was not afraid of anybody.

Now, when I walk into a doctor's office, I come as a colleague. I am the officer in charge of my treatment. After a few minutes batting the medical ball back and forth over the net with me, my latest new doctor asked, "What kind of work do you do?" "Don't worry," I replied, "I'm not a doctor, and I'm not a lawyer."

As I was afflicted with a so-called "rare" cancer, I also had to maneuver through a batallion of local doctors who, while sounding extremely persuasive, had very little information about my cancer and only palliative treatment to offer me. What does "palliative" mean? It is treatment intended to help relieve the symptoms of terminal cancer patients. In other words, no cure for you, you are going to die."

As I countered their objections one by one, I began to suspect that some of what passed for medical advice was actually a bureaucratic reaction to a potentially costly situation.

The health insurer, with a primary mission of cost containment, was subjecting me to a strategy of exhaustion. Perhaps a better word for it would be "strategy of annihilation." If cost containment was the imperative, their primary goal was then to get me and my expensive and difficult cancer to just go away. Have no treatment, have locally available treatment, have only palliative treatment. And die—the sooner, the better.

Of course, in the modern world, the doctor who is a provider for the insurance company must answer to the insurance company. And my insurer set up an escalating set of roadblocks as I pressed on to receive treatment, curative treatment. Their first plan was really no plan at all: Let's sit around and wait to see how fast it grows—that deceptively benign expression—"watchful waiting." In other words, fiddling while Rome burns. Sitting around eating bon bons while your belly fills with cancer.

Friends often said, "You must spend a lot of time angry and resentful, bemoaning your fate and asking, "Why me?" Never. I have felt—since day one—that this mission, in all its particulars, was tailor-made for me.

Not for me the standard breast cancer or colon cancer, where you have to follow the regimen prescribed by your local health insurer and either live or die by it. Instead, I am issued this crazy appendix cancer—pseudomyxoma peritonei. It doesn't look like any other cancer, it doesn't act like any other cancer, and I have to engage in a spelling bee every time anybody asks what I have.

Knowing what I know now, I would follow the same path of questioning the medical and insurance powers-that-be, doing my own research, finding the world's expert on my illness/injury, exploring all options, pressing on until I received the finest care—even if I had the most common cancer in the world.

As the weeks pass after my diagnosis and the plot thickens, I will be required to engage in high-level diplomacy with my doctors until they think that it was their idea to refer me to an out-of-network expert. Befuddled by conflicting diagnoses, I will have to deploy persuasive letters to expert surgeons all over the country, soliciting their assistance and advice. Then, as I am single, self-employed, out of business and out of funds, I will need to muster up a network and call upon it for everything from haircuts to frequent flyer miles. After I have been accepted for treatment by the world's expert in appendix cancer, my health insurer will say, "No way, we won't pay!"

So . . . I will have to go on the offense. I will turn myself *into the finest lawyer that money can buy, read the studies, make the phone calls, twist the arms. And write a document so powerful that the only thing left for my health insurer to ask is, "Where do we send the money?"*

Researching, writing, persuading. Outsmarting the smarties. Perfecting my strategy. Exposing the hidden agendas. These are my very best skills . . . I relish using them. I am the Warrior Queen of persuasive letter-writing; and there is no bureaucracy that can stonewall me. I will make a hundred phone calls—scheming, scamming, playing my little chess game—until I find the double agent within the bureaucracy who will help me win the battle. Why me? I am uniquely qualified for the mission.

It took me three months to secure my expert, face off against the health insurer, write the appeal and emerge victorious. Another nine months was spent undergoing two massive surgeries plus chemotherapy, getting myself declared officially geezered by Social Security Disability and finding my new physical and emotional bearings in the Land of the Living.

Yes, during this year I have often been in Bad Trouble. More than once I slid perilously close to death. However, my year of cancer turned out to be my finest hour. I did the highest-paid, most exhilarating and worthwhile work of my life. I won the respect of doctors, lawyers, bureaucrats of all types and stripes. During the dark nights and long days, I was sustained by the love of family, associates and friends. I won great victories decisively. After the Clash of the Titans with the health insurer was over and the dust had settled, my bill for a year of massive medical intervention—two major abdominal surgeries, chemotherapy and over a month in hospital—was nine dollars. Not nine-hundred thousand, not nine thousand, but NINE.

After the asking for help and the receiving of help comes the giving of help. It's natural, like seed to flower to fruit.

Within a week of winning my appeal, another person popped up in my town, with my "rare" cancer, at my same HMO. Michael and Sandy lived about ten minutes from me. What could I do . . . I galloped over there on my white horse, told them everything, handed over my appeal and said, "Take it, use it, plagiarize it. Ride in on my coat-tails." Michael threw my name around at the HMO, and they paid for his out-of-network treatment with nary a peep. Michael and Sandy said, "How can we thank you, what would we have done without you, etc., etc.?" I replied, "Helping you makes my suffering worthwhile." Sandy dubbed my insurance appeal "Laurie's War Documents." Thus began my career as the Insurance Warrior.

New people are appearing every week with a variety of cancers. They ask me, "How could my doctor not know? How could my insurer not pay for my treatment? Could my doctor be wrong? How could my doctor recommend a treatment that is not the current standard of care for my disease? How come I learned all about this disease on the Web in twenty minutes, and my doctor says that nobody knows anything about it?" "Shocking, isn't it?" I say, "First, you need to fire the doctor who will not work with you to find the best treatment. If your doctor knows nothing about your illness, you need to run, not walk, to an expert."

Within a two-week period recently, I engaged in insurance appeals with three "helpees." We had five days to defeat Blue Cross—we did it in four. We had a month to make Cigna cry uncle—they gave up in three weeks. Then, a couple came to me with military insurance. I seriously questioned whether we could bully them into paying, and whether the patient himself would be able to rise up and fight the military bureaucracy which had sustained him for twenty-four years. I did my usual research. Then, for the first time, I applied some serious tough-love: "This is your hero's journey. You can either do what I say, or pay a malpractice lawyer $20,000 to do it!" I admonished them. Within two days, the military insurance was vanquished, and he was on his way to his lifesaving treatment.

Somehow, after those two weeks of glorious victories, people with other cancers and conditions began to find me. Esophageal cancer, pancreatic cancer, mulitple myeloma, splenic marginal zone lymphoma. I have learned more with each case, but I always use the same battle plan and the same tactics. Often, the insurer keeps up their refusals until the day before the surgery . . . the strategy of exhaustion. We are still fighting while the patient is preparing to go under the knife.

I have never lost a case. The insurer always, always pays. I am not a lawyer, and I do not propose to turn you into one. I am not a medical billing and coding expert; you do not have to be one, either. You are fighting cancer, it is a week before your surgery date, and the insurance states that they are not going to pay. You do not need a comprehensive course in the fine points of insurance law. What you need is the crash course, the quick-and-dirty, cut-and-paste, hit-and-run method of making the insurance company do the right thing. It's all you need.

I had no job, no money, no lawyer in the family. I had no partner, nobody to fight my battles for me. I knew nothing about medical malpractice law nor about the inner workings of insurance companies. And yet, I was able to secure treatment from the finest, most renowned surgeon in the world for my disease.

By my own efforts, I turned "two good years" into an 80% chance of twenty good years. It was a huge, terrifying, potentially fatal war that I had to fight. The best that I could do was put my head down, embrace the battle, and forge ahead. Don't get me wrong . . . I'm not ready to get down on my knees and thank my health insurer for the learning experience. However, this has turned out to be the most empowering experience of my life.

You can do the same; it will be even easier for you.

This is an advice book for anyone who finds himself in the Army of the Seriously Afflicted, or who finds a friend or loved one there. In other words, it is a book for everyone. It is a book for anyone who will ever tangle with their health insurer —in time, most of us will. I will share with you the fruits of my labors: the letters that made the phone ring, the appeal which made the HMO roll over and cry uncle. The approach, the tricks, the ways around the bureaucracy. You are Shameless and Blameless now, and I will show you how to exploit every opportunity. Whom to call, whom to write and exactly what to say that will spur the bureaucracy into action.

Welcome to the war of Big Medical Involvement. If we live long enough, most of us will be drafted and serve there. Some have said, "You scare us. You are too blunt. You must give us hope." There are many books that offer hope: the Chicken Soup *series, the* Kitchen Table Wisdom *books. They do this much better than me. This book is a field guide; it will show you the maneuvers and give you the weapons to survive the slings and arrows that your insurance company and its foot-soldiers will hurl at you.*

You are the raw recruits, and I am the drill sergeant. Is the drill sergeant sweet and gentle with the new soldiers? Does the drill sergeant say, "I hope you win the war?"

No. He is relentless and tough; he whips them into shape. He gives them the weapons which they will need to actually win the battles and survive the war. Without these weapons, there is no hope. With these weapons, you can win the war, receive your lifesaving treatment, and return home to ponder the notion of hope in peace and health.

Let me be the fierce voice, the one who exhorts you to put on your warrior garb and prepare to come out of this struggle with your dignity, your self-respect, and your bank account intact. And, far more important, to come out of it alive.

My helpees have taught me that the loving pep-talk is as valuable as the information. Perhaps more. One of the guiding principles of military strategy is: "Maintain positive morale even in the face of set-backs." So, I will share just enough of my own story to light a fire under you. Then, I will follow with all of the Grand Strategy, tactics, maneuvers, diplomacy, tricks of deception. (Yes, deception—All's fair in love and war!) that you will need to win your own fine victory.

CHAPTER 2

Prelude to Battle:

Clarify Your Mission

"I think I would have visited the doctor a little sooner," delivered by a friend as we sat having tea after my first operation. She had just finished questioning me . . . what were my symptoms, how long had I been having them, what had finally caused me to get medical advice.

Was I in denial? Of course I was. Just like every other oblivious person waltzing around in the Land of the Living. Who thinks that they will be getting appendix cancer? Who even heard of appendix cancer?

But there is something deeper. The organism simply does not want to believe that it could be in Bad Trouble. The muscles, the immune system, the orchestra of organs inside who make up the living community that is us, send us messages that something is Bad Wrong. But, at the same time, they deny it. We, the organs, do not want something to be Bad Wrong with us. Maybe a food allergy. Symptoms of menopause. Diabetes, perhaps?

So . . . do you believe that you would have the presence of mind to sort out sooner than I the mixed messages of the living organism?

I first started feeling poorly about ten years before All This started. At the time, I was a massage therapist, working at a health club, doing six massages a day, five days a week. One Sunday I realized that I never felt rested, never felt well. I was forty-five years old. I was doing a massage marathon every day . . . ample reason to be exhausted, yes?

I continued on in this fashion for ten more years. Then, one day, I noticed that I was even more tired than usual. Really tired, dragging-yourself-around tired. Bone-weary.

Like many people in the modern world, I could only afford a catastrophic health insurance policy with a sky-high deductible, so I thought twice before ever darkening the door of the HMO. I called them to find out if a physical exam would be subject to the deductible. The financial advice person clued me in, "We will pay 80% for a routine physical, not subject to deductible. However, you must not ask any questions about your health. Do not breathe a word of it. If you bring up any concerns whatsoever, it will become a medical visit and you will have to pay cash out of pocket for it." Go to the doctor but don't ask any medical questions . . . right.

In I went, convinced that I would be diagnosed with diabetes. After doing a thorough exam and blood work, the doctor pronounced me the healthiest fifty-five-year-old on the planet. Three months later, I would be undergoing emergency surgery for cancer which had spread throughout the abdomen.

I had a clean bill of health. If you were me, would you have done more?

One day I opened my office door to a client who had been a nurse for forty years. She took one look at me and said, "Oh no. Something is wrong." The next day, I marched myself, my gaunt face and my huge stomach into the HMO. I didn't have any trouble persuading them that there was something Bad Wrong with me.

* * *

You have been drafted—this is the prelude to the battle.

Size up your opponent

The "beat the insurer" books that I studied during my Clash of the Titans with the insurance company all emphasized the importance of scrutinizing your benefits booklet and choosing your insurance carefully.

CHOOSING YOUR INSURANCE??? Who has any choice about their insurance anymore? HMO, PPO . . . like so many other aspects of insurance these days, it is pretty much all illusion. All insurances have co-pays (sometimes for everything), deductibles (sometimes multiple deductibles for different services), co-insurances. Some have prescription drug coverage, some do not. However, prescription coverage may also be an illusion.

Have you ever heard of a *formulary?* That is the list of prescription drugs that your insurer covers. Can you guess which drugs do not appear on the formulary, and therefore are not covered? The most common ones and the most expensive ones.

I recently saw a story on the news . . . a couple in their fifties, she had brain cancer. They had "top-of-the-line" health insurance, and they were both working when All This started for them. She had undergone two surgeries for brain cancer, and she had had to stop working. The drugs for her cancer cost $16,000 per month. Gee, do you suppose those drugs were on the formulary?

The couple had already spent most of their savings and had completely depleted his 401K. They were getting ready to sell their house to pay for her care.

I don't know if any insurer anywhere would have paid for her chemotherapy drug . . . it was just too expensive. What could they have done? Find the right decision-maker at the drug company and write a brilliant letter throwing themselves on their mercy and asking for the drug at a reduced rate. Write a brilliant appeal to the insurer, pointing out all the mistakes that had been made during her medical treatment and requesting that they pay for the drug. If all else failed, I would spend down all of my assets, get on Medicaid, and save my house.

Get the Insurance Commissioner mixed up in it. Go to the media. Go all out. This is war, people!

So . . . what to do if you are "choosing" insurance, once you know that you are really not covered for the most devastating drugs, treatments, or surgeries no matter what insurance you choose? Take a deep breath, read the fine print, and go right to the bottom line . . . THE LIFETIME MAXIMUM.

As far as I am concerned, the lifetime cap is the biggest pitfall hidden in our health insurance. Lifetime caps were part of the grand scheme called "managed care," which was dreamed up in the early 1970s in order to curb spiraling healthcare costs. To me, "managed care" really means "limited care" and/or "care denied." The lifetime cap is the way for the insurer to limit costs for each and every patient. After the lifetime maximum is reached, you are cut off. No notice, no ceremony . . . cut off. Are you in the hospital when you reach your maximum? Tough luck . . . cut off. If you cap out your insurance while you are hospitalized, they will keep treating you. However, while you are recuperating at home, you will start receiving bills for $18,000 . . . $92,000 . . . $247,000.

What kind of insanity is this? How are people supposed to pay mammoth bills when they just got out of the hospital, haven't worked in months, and probably cannot work now? Obviously, the actuaries or insurance executives who instituted these measures didn't think beyond their guiding principle: cost containment.

A pretty standard lifetime maximum in 1970 was one million dollars. Over the last thirty years, healthcare costs have sky-rocketed. Not only has "managed care" not solved healthcare cost inflation, it has undoubtedly contributed to it. It would cost you $18 million to buy the same services today. Take a look at your benefits booklet—I'll bet that your lifetime maximum is nowhere near $18 million. If your insurance is anything like mine, the cap is $2 million.

If you have cancer, a heart transplant, a serious injury, ongoing expensive treatments/medication, you can easily run through $2 million dollars in six months to a year.

In my dealings with health insurers, I have found that just about everything is negotiable except the lifetime cap. About the only way to overcome the lifetime maximum would be to prove that they had grievously injured you, and that your ongoing treatment was THEIR FAULT.

The lifetime cap is, in my estimation, the most important

variable in your health insurance policy. If you can find a policy with a cap of more than $2 million, go for it.

People believe that health insurance is like a store. There is a television set in the store with a marked price of $100. If you want the television, you must pay $100. WRONG. Health insurance is like a swap meet . . . you will argue and haggle and horse-trade back and forth. And, ultimately, YOU will decide what treatment you are going to get and how much your insurer is going to pay for it.

Clarify your mission

I did not go to the doctor sooner, partly because I had my priorities wrong. I had no money, and a policy with a high deductible. This was enough to keep me from going to the doctor until it was nearly too late. Granted, I would not have been saved from my appendix cancer even if I had marched into the HMO and hollered and screamed about exhaustion years before my crisis. No health insurer is going to give you a CT scan for a complaint of exhaustion. However, it wouldn't have been quite such a dire emergency if I had received treatment six months or a year before.

Don't be like me—penny wise and pound foolish. We all have high deductibles. Get to the doctor if you feel strongly that something is Bad Wrong; and lean on them until they do all possible diagnostic tests for you.

My larger point is this. As you advance further into the Clash of the Titans against the health insurer, remember that—for you—it is not about money. Your objective—your only objective—is to get the best and most effective treatment for your disease/condition.

Of course, you would like to save your bank account and your house if you can. However, if you give all your money, you lose your house, they are billing you for $100,000—but you got your treatment—you won. If you are still alive after your treatment, so much the better.

If you're dead because you did not get the finest healthcare available, you lost.

Guard against subversion

Do not let anyone blame you for your disease. I was surprised, dismayed, and discouraged by how many of my nearest and dearest felt the need to suggest that I caused my own cancer. They do this for several reasons, and they do it in several different ways.

I do not believe that people mean to blame us for our cancer. They probably do not realize that they are doing it. As a matter of fact, it took me awhile to figure out why I walked away from so many coffee sessions feeling blamed.

Some blame you in order to get themselves off the hook. My beloved psychologist and life mentor asked me, "Where did your life go so disastrously wrong?" Then, he asked me questions about what had been going on the last few years and said, "You must have been too far gone before you ever got to me." Gee, thanks.

Some quiz you about your symptoms, attitudes, habits, etc. to make sure that you were doing something which THEY have never done. They make it quite clear that they believe that whatever you were doing/thinking caused your cancer; therefore, they are exempt.

Newsflash! Nobody has a magic charm to protect them from Bad Medical Trouble. People with long-lived family members get cancer. Vegetarians get cancer. Neurotic people get cancer, emotionally healthy people get cancer. Old people, young people—all get cancer. Wise people get cancer, right along with the foolish ones. Couch potatoes get cancer, and Olympic athletes get cancer. People with much still to do in this life get cancer, as do people who are finished here on earth.

In my capacity as the Insurance Warrior, I have investigated various "rare" cancers. I pulled up the website for multiple myeloma . . . on the home page, it said, "More and more people are getting this disease younger and younger." A week later, I looked up esophageal cancer, "More and more people are getting this rare cancer younger and younger." A few days after that, someone popped up with splenic marginal zone lymphoma: "More and more people are getting this cancer younger and younger." Two weeks later, a friend came down with prostate cancer; I consulted the *AMA Medical Guide*: "By the age of eighty, virtually every male has it. . . ."[1]

Is anyone connecting the dots? I am saying that more and more people are coming down with cancer, and they are doing it younger and younger.

I am not saying that you are going to die of your cancer. Many of us modern cancer patients are doing just fine years later, thank you very much. But, sorry . . . people who have a clean bill from the doctor get cancer, too.

---

1 The American Medical Association: *Family Medical Guide*, Random House, 1987.

Many cancers sneak up on you. There is no affordable or non-invasive test for them, and they have no symptoms. 90% of people with my type of cancer get diagnosed by having the wrong surgery for the wrong thing. Surgery which greatly reduces their chance of a good outcome.

Never let anyone blame you for your disease. You have enough to concern yourself about. If your friend tells you that she would surely have heeded the warnings sooner, smile and say, "I am sure that, when you are faced with this, you will do a much better job than I."

Take the bull by the horns

When my oncologist told me that there was no treatment, and that I had two good years left, my first impulse was to do some research and find out if this was really true. It turned out not to be true. Since then, I have learned that not every patient reacts this way. Many would not conceive of questioning their doctor. They would accept the two years with grace, suffer and die on schedule.

Do not take your health insurer's word for anything—and that includes your in-network doctor. Ask questions until there are no more questions to ask. Listen not only to the answers, but to HOW your doctor answers. Does he sound offended by your questions, or does he honor your questions and concerns? Have you done your own research before asking your questions, and do his answers make sense to you?

Write down everything that is said to you—every doctor visit, every phone call.

Never wait to "hear back" from your health insurer . . . you will be dead or all better before they ever get back to you.

Pester them, challenge them, hold their feet to the fire. Do it all in writing with a copy to the Insurance Commissioner.

This is all-out war.

CHAPTER 3

Medical Boot Camp:

Let Truth Be Your Guide

The day after my first visit to the doctor, I reported back for a CT scan. As I offered up my wrist for the plastic ID bracelet, I felt as though I were participating in a secret ceremony, swearing me into the Army of the Seriously Afflicted and Medically Involved.

As the toxic iodine flowed through my veins, making me flush and my heart beat faster, I wondered what this body would undergo in the weeks and months to come. All I could think was, "Train wreck, train wreck, Bad Wrong, Bad Wrong."

I reported back to the doctor's office the following morning to hear my verdict. An old friend insisted on accompanying me to the appointment; I protested, not knowing yet that it is not wise to go to Icky Doctor Appointments by oneself.

Since I rarely went to the doctor, I knew no physician at the HMO. So, the doctor with the lean, intelligent face was a stranger to me. "What do you think is wrong?" she asked. "I think it's really bad," I answered. "It is," she said, holding my gaze. "You don't know me," she added, "All I can do is tell you this, woman to woman. You most likely have Stage

III or Stage IV ovarian cancer." Long pause, while the color drained from my face. "Do people survive this?" I asked. "Oh, all the time," she answered. I was soon to learn that doctors burdened with dire news sometimes put a happy spin on things, saving the bad news for the oncologist to deliver.

She went on to describe the horror scene that was my belly—tumors, fluid, who-knows-what disgusting flotsam and jetsam of cancer packing the abdomen. "Is it ever not cancerous?" I asked. "Rarely . . . A friend of mine had something like this, and it turned out to be benign." That happy spin again, the loophole, the main chance. Then she told me how to schedule the surgery and left us alone.

My friend said, "I'm going to pray that it is benign." I was furious. I shot back, "Don't waste your breath. It is cancer. Is God supposed to magically turn it benign overnight? If you want to pray, pray for me to have the best surgeon to fix this mess."

Over the next three days, the stomach grew exponentially. I woke in the middle of the night, drenched with sweat and short of breath, feeling the hand of death on me. My hands and feet grew cold . . . my life was draining out of me. And the phone started ringing off the hook—twenty calls in one hour. How am I, what is going on, what is the diagnosis, do I need groceries? How can I bear to tell the same terrible story again and again? How am I to manage this barrage of phone calls, speaking as I am from inside my own nightmare?

I, who have been a nice, polite, caretaking gal all my life, put a message on my phone: "If you are a doctor with the HMO, I would like very much for you to leave a message. If you are anybody else, I DON'T GIVE A RAT'S ASS!"

And, so, for the first time, I spoke with my real voice, the voice of rage. The rage of the creature dying before its time. I don't want to die, not here, not now—not this way. Unbeknownst to me, that telephone message would be a time bomb with unexpected fall-out. Some loved the message, calling just to hear it, "Yay, you," they said much later, "Finally speaking up for yourself." Others left a message in spite of me, showing that they understood, "Well, I do give a rat's ass, and I'm leaving one anyhow!" But another small faction hated the message, caught my terrible anger, and lobbed it right back over the net at me. The volley ended there, I am pleased to say, because I really didn't give a rat's ass.

I called my sister, the R.N.—all the way across the country—and said, "Please don't say good-bye. Can't we talk a little longer?" She realized that I was in trouble, got on the next plane, and flew to my side.

We went down the foxhole and into the battle zone together. My sister became my brigadier general—living in my house, driving my car, cleaning my cupboards—and helping me to survive The First Surgery.

Our initial round of doctor visits included the pre-operative check-up, blood tests, anesthesia meeting and so on. Come to find out that I had fallen ill at the wrong time; all of the cancer surgeons were in Florida, attending a conference and, I supposed, sipping mai tais. The OB/GYN doctor said, "Maybe we can schedule the surgery in a week or two," thus giving me my first opportunity to say "no" to a doctor.

"No," I said, "I can barely breathe. I can't eat. I am doing my best, but I cannot last that long." A surgeon flew in on the red-eye—the show would go on in two days.

There was no time to meet my surgeon-to-be, no time for pleasantries. I met him for the first time just outside the operating room—he materialized next to my gurney in a very stylish business suit. Perhaps it was the Ativan talking, or perhaps it was not, but I blurted out a speech the like of which no surgeon has ever heard before: "I am standing in a shining cathedral of Truth, and I am looking at it with my eyes wide open." I had never been more at peace in my life. And, in that moment, I conceived a new appreciation for truth—a love of truth which remains fierce to this day.

❋ ❋ ❋

Truth is your comrade

In the most life-threatening moments of Bad Medical Trouble, I was always comforted by the truth. I could rest in the truth. The fact that my local doctors and insurance bureaucrats were not telling me the truth somehow infuriated me more than the fact that they were trying to prevent me from getting any treatment which might save my life. The ceaseless quest for truth brought me some peace, saved my life, and lead me to help others to reach the same solid rock.

In generations past, doctors and families often withheld the truth from the patient, offering all sorts of false reassurances about his condition. I cannot think of a lonelier, sadder, more miserable state than dying with everyone lying to you. I am convinced that people know when they are dying. If you are dying, and nobody tells the truth, you do the knowing and the dying alone.

In your upcoming battle against the health insurer,

truth will be your sword and your shield. The best way, the easiest way, the finest way to achieve your objective—to get the treatment—is to confront your opponent with a shining mountain of facts.

I know that there are those who go through Bad Medical Trouble without befriending the truth. They are the ones who are fortunate enough to have a partner or family member to fight for them, do the research, make the decisions, etc. I must say, though, that I feel that this entire journey went more easily for me because I had to sort it out myself, own it, and speak my truth as best I could.

Anger is part of war

Cancer victims are supposed to be kind, grateful . . . inspiring. People expect us to bemoan our fate, but they certainly aren't ready to deal with our anger.

I had a fierce bout of anger at my mother. And, boy oh boy, did she lob it back over the net. Expect the possibility that you will go gonzo on your nearest and dearest, or that they will suddenly turn on you. The good news here is that, if you can realize that anger is a side-effect of war, nobody will take it personally or turn it into a family feud.

Friends, on the other hand, don't have to hang with you through your anger. Many friends will drop away during your long siege with cancer, and anger is one of the reasons why they disappear.

I couldn't indulge in anger at my health insurer. I had to remain open to their concerns and dispassionate in my approach to them in order to persuade them to pay. Instead, my anger was directed at the friends who blamed, bothered, misunderstood and deserted me.

Once the anger towards the friends began to subside, anger crept back in through the back door. As I turned my energies toward helping people to win their insurance fights, I began to criticize and judge other people's choices of doctors and treatments, feeling that I knew best.

It is not easy even now to admit how my own ego fed the anger monster. Suffice it to say that, for me, anger has been part of the cancer experience. It is good, I believe, to be on the lookout for it, so that it doesn't gather momentum and wreak its own havoc. And, when feelings are running high, it is good to be able to notice the anger, not to visit it unnecessarily on our nearest and dearest, and to forgive ourselves for it.

It took long months and a lot of willingness to accept that anger is part of the illness—it's a package deal. Anger can pass like a thunderstorm or linger like air pollution. While I am accountable for my own anger, what other people do about my disease is 100% about them.

Choose your comrades wisely

Weed out the rubber-neckers and the weepers and the nay-sayers and the ones who tell you what to pray for. I never asked that friend who took me to the first doctor appointment to take me again. I would better have gone alone. From then on, my sister-in-arms was Hillary. Nothing fazes Hillary. She accepts everyone, just as they are. When I emerged from my icky doctor appointments, Hillary had befriended everyone in the waiting room. It was a veritable party out there! We would walk to the car, I would tell the latest ghastly news, and Hillary would pull out her Magic Coupon Book—a book the size of the phone book. She would find a discount coupon for some little hole-in-the-wall restaurant in whatever neighborhood we were that day, and we would have lunch.

Now is the time to protect yourself . . . choose your comrades wisely.

Don't let anyone tell you what to pray for

My friend wanted to pray that my cancer was benign. I thought this was ridiculous.

Since then, I have encountered many cancer patients and family members who pray for outcomes. "I prayed that the tumor would be taken away," "I prayed that his CT scan would be clear," "I prayed that the surgery would turn out well."

I understand that praying for a specific result is comforting and empowering to some. For myself, I simply do not understand this praying for outcomes. The cancer often recurs, the scans often show tumor, and the surgery is often not a cure. When people pray for outcomes, they seem so often to be devastated when those outcomes do not come to pass.

Why did God not answer my prayers? Am I bad? Does God not care about me? Does God even exist?

I rarely prayed for outcomes. First, I don't believe that the universe works like that: you pray for a Cadillac, and God puts one in your driveway. It has never worked that way for me; and I want to make it OK for others who feel the same way.

Second, I am not always the best judge of what the highest and best outcome would be. After all, some of the finest developments in my life have evolved from events which seemed, at the time, disastrous.

Third, I don't want to waste my energy praying for something which may not come to pass.

I pray instead for peace. My prayer is always answered.

CHAPTER 4

Commanding Officer:

Qualify Your Doctor

After the first surgery, strange things began to happen. Assisting surgeons appeared at my bedside, saying, "You know, it just doesn't look like ovarian cancer . . . not sure what it is . . . not so aggressive, not invasive . . . I feel good about this . . . slides sent to Johns Hopkins."

And so I spent a week in the hospital, sick in a way that I had never been sick before. It is the sick that comes from major surgery. There was no pain in it. However, the only symptom that the doctors and nurses inquired about was my "pain level." I don't have any, I answered, twenty or thirty times a day.

What I did have was a terrible weakness, a total lack of initiative, and a constant sense of dread. It was as if my deepest body-regulating systems—autonomic nervous system, neurotransmitters, brain stem—were in a total uproar. The dials were spinning out of control, and I was overwhelmed by the flood of appalling messages coming up from the depths. I was a raw nerve.

The first time that they forced me to walk, I made it to the nurses' station, then passed out and went down like a sack of potatoes. I woke up on the floor with doctors and nurses peering down at me. Somehow I found the courage to walk again. They eventually took the staples out, and my sister brought me home.

Three days later, Sis and I were lounging around the living room, watching court shows on TV. The OB/GYN surgeon was calling, "The results have come back from Johns Hopkins. It is not cancer . . . what you have is benign."

Not cancer. We immediately set about calling family and friends to give them the incredible news. OK, I had a huge surgery, but now my ordeal is over.

Another week passed, I gradually grew strong enough to climb the stairs, fix lunch, worry about money. My sister returned to her home across the country, and I set about recuperating in earnest. Within four weeks, I was running a mile a day. And within six weeks, I borrowed some frequent flyer miles and flew to Arizona for a week of swimming, cactus-watching and looking into the desert to find my spirit.

I returned from Arizona a relaxed, recharged person, ready for my first post-op visit with the surgeon. Or so I thought.

I found the penthouse office of my surgeon with its tasteful flower arrangements, soft voices and panoramic view. Nurses in matching uniforms ushered me into the examining room. Surely he will say, "Incision looks fine, you are a champ, have a nice life."

The surgeon comes in, shakes my hand and says, "So,

you're working with the oncologists at the HMO*?" "No . . . "*
I say, color once again draining out of my face, "Dr. Smith
told me that I didn't have cancer." At that moment the nurse
called him away for a phone call, and I had five minutes
to ponder the implications. There is no way around it—this
doctor is going to tell me that, contrary to what Dr. Smith
and Johns Hopkins have decreed, I do have cancer. Who ever
heard of such a thing? It was as if one doctor had taken
away the cancer, only to have this one give it back to me.

Finally he returned, "You HAVE *cancer," he said, sounding*
exasperated, "We are just arguing semantics here." Semantics?
He explained that the cancer that I have, pseudomyxoma
peritonei—appendix cancer—is not as aggressive or invasive
as some cancers. Therefore, it is sometimes called "benign."
Great . . . I have the only benign cancer in the universe. He
gave me odds of 30% chance of recurrence in five years. I
knew nothing yet. So, if I was going to have cancer again,
30% sounded do-able to me.

One said I had cancer, one said I didn't. It was Friday
afternoon. I left the surgeon's office, stopped for tacos, then
came home and made a beeline for the computer. I typed in
"pseudomyxoma peritonei" and got to work.

I went to the sources . . . read articles and studies in
the Annals of Surgical Oncology, *the* European Journal of
Surgical Oncology. *There were many different types of*
pseudomyxoma, all of which would certainly kill me without
further treatment. Hmmm . . . I guess that "watchful waiting"
is not such a good idea.

One name cropped up everywhere I looked—Dr. Paul
Sugarbaker. He had started thirty-five years ago as a colon

cancer surgeon at NIH, then put together a unique surgery and chemotherapy approach, applying the heated chemotherapy agents directly to the organs during the operation. He had performed this surgery over nine hundred times over twenty-five years, with a 70% rate of no recurrence for fifteen years on patients with my type of the disease.

All of a sudden I felt like Chicken Little, running around asking if the sky was falling. These doctors with their ovarian cancer and their months to live and their no cancer and their 30% could not all be right. And yet, each one spoke as if he were absolutely sure. My eyes were opened; I resolved in that moment never to accept anything a doctor said to me without questioning until I had no more questions to ask. And then, find some more questions and ask some more.

A few weeks later, I had a follow-up appointment with Dr. Smith. I said, "I have been to see Dr. Jones. You do know that I have cancer, don't you? Why did you tell me that I don't have cancer?" He looked at the floor and said, "I figured that I would leave it to Dr. Jones to fill you in on the details." Details.

* * *

Different doctors are giving you different diagnoses and different prognoses . . . you don't know whom to believe. You have been on the Internet enough to know that there IS curative treatment for your disease. You have begun to realize that nobody is managing your case but you. You are the general, in command of all operations. How do you find the right doctor?

How not to choose a doctor

These are all real examples. . . . I have seen people choose a surgeon for complex, difficult, lifesaving surgery based on the following:

• My primary care physician, whom I have never met before, recommended him.

We're talking about surgery that could either save your life or ruin your life; you are going to take the word of someone you don't know? Your PMP (primary care physician) is a key gatekeeper for the insurance company. He may have a vested interest in referring you to a physician who in contracted with the insurer—and thus paid at a reduced rate.

One day, I was browsing a list of insurance terminology on a state Insurance Commissioner's website. The definition of the word "gatekeeper" was "primary care physician." To some degree, he is tasked with controlling costs. One way to accomplish this is to keep you away from expensive specialists and to keep you in the network.

• My oncologist referred me to him.

Your oncologist is part of the same bureaucracy. He doesn't want any trouble, he knows that they will say no to any unusual or out-of-network requests. He may be motivated to go out of his way for you, but don't assume that he will. His life will be easier if you accept whatever cookie-cutter treatments the network has to offer, putting your affairs in order, and not ruffling any feathers.

- He operated on my daughter's friend for a different type of cancer; the friend died.

Please explain to me why you would rush to a surgeon who operated on a friend of a family member. Particularly if the patient DIED. Death is not a good outcome. OK, I understand that, with serious cancer treatment, death is sometimes inevitable. However, having the patients die is not the best recommendation up front. Besides, you know absolutely nothing about this surgeon . . . whether he has any expertise at all in the type of surgery that you are planning. The doctor may be a fine breast cancer surgeon; however, if you have esophageal cancer, and he operates on you, the consequences might not be so good.

- Somebody in my support group/cancer group/cancer forum said he was good.

Word of mouth like that is good enough for a hairdresser; it is not good enough for someone who is going to cut you open or prescribe powerful medications. Of course, other patients' experience will factor into your decision. I am simply suggesting that you also do your own research about your doctor of choice.

- He is in my town/county/state.

He is close by to my house. My friends and family members live here, and they can help me while I am in the hospital. That's fine if you are getting surgery for bunions. It's not fine if you are seeking treatment for a rare/complicated/difficult cancer.

I'm tough on this point. I have visited people lying for months in the hospital bed because of post-surgical complications. They chose a surgeon because the surgeon was close by. The surgery was botched; they were ruined. All doctors are not created equal.

Disclaimer, disclaimer . . . under certain circumstances, having friends and family near to you may be more important than seeing the doctor with the very best numbers and the most cutting-edge treatments. Your family is key to recovery. If you stay close to home, your family can also help each other.

All I am suggesting is that you not choose an expert physician for your lifesaving treatment based on geography ALONE.

- He is a provider for my insurance.

Tell me that you will not choose a doctor just because he is a provider for your health insurer. We know now that it is possible to leap over the prohibitions stated in your benefits booklet, and choose based on your own research and best wisdom.

I know that it sounds counter-intuitive, but—if my life is at stake—I would rather be treated by a doctor who is NOT a provider for my insurance. Why? Because I know that the insurance-provider doctor is employed by the insurance company. He may make recommendations for my care based on what he knows that they will pay for, not what will be best for me. I would prefer to do the hard fighting, make my insurance pay for the out-of-network expert, and know that that physician is not beholden to the insurance company.

If there is a doctor in your insurance network who is as well-qualified as any other expert, congratulate yourself and sign up for an appointment. Always making sure, of course, that the treatments which he recommends are not just the most affordable, or the most available in the network, but the most likely to give you a long, quality life.

Certainly, there are fine physicians within every insurance network who will go out of their way, do the extra research, stand up for your best interests. I merely suggest that you approach all doctor decisions with the attitude of "buyer beware."

• **He practices at a world-renowned cancer center.**

He practices at a world-renowned cancer center. I have seen people with all types of cancer flock to the Mayo Clinics, the Sloan-Ketterings, the famous university medical centers of this world. They assume that, since these institutions are so well-known, they must be good at everything. WRONG. I have seen people with my "rare" cancer offered all sorts of inappropriate and ineffective treatments at world-class cancer centers, until they were ruined and there was no chance for them at all.

There is nothing wrong with going to the Mayo Clinic . . . just make sure to qualify and interview your doctor no matter where he practices. Don't assume, just because the doctor practices at a famous medical center, that he is expert, experienced, or has good outcomes treating your disease/condition.

How to qualify a doctor

Qualifying a doctor is a three-step process. Very simple, you can accomplish it in an hour.

First, go to the Internet and search ("google") the doctor's name. All sorts of websites will pop up. Look for the medical center website where the doctor has his practice. Somewhere on that website, you will find "physicians," "physician profiles," or "physician bios." This is your doctor's resumé, his curriculum vitae. It will tell you his training, accomplishments, special interests and attainments.

I know it's hard to believe, but I have seen people go to a thoracic surgeon for complicated abdominal surgery. The results were not good. It takes only five minutes to find your doctor's resumé and to get a general idea of his areas of expertise.

Second, make an appointment to interview the doctor, either in person or by phone. Ask him the questions that matter to you about his experience and approach. I would ask the following:

- How many of these surgeries/treatments have you done?

- How many patients with my disease/condition are you currently treating?

- What are your outcomes with these patients? Do you have any studies/papers that I can read?

- What medications/surgical procedures do you normally prescribe for this disease/condition? Why?

You are interested in the answers to these questions, but you are also interested in HOW he answers the questions. Is he haughty? Dismissive? Uncomfortable? Or does he patiently answer your questions and address your concerns? Which of your questions bother him the most? If he is the right doctor, he should be at ease answering any reasonable questions which you might have, and his answers should make sense to you. If he is the right doctor, he will respect you for ensuring that he is qualified to have your life in his hands.

And, third, go to the National Institutes of Health (NIH) website and see if your doctor of choice has published any articles or studies in the medical journals. They maintain a free database called "PubMed" where you can search for journal articles. From the studies, you can tell what the doctor's approach is, how accomplished he is in his field, what are his outcomes.

Bear in mind, however, that the fact that your doctor of choice has not published does not mean that he is not an excellent clinician. Reading studies by your expert doctor is just one more way to learn about his stature and his approach. If you find papers authored by your doctor of choice, file them away. You may need them as proof when you are writing your appeal.

You can also use the PubMed database to FIND an expert doctor. Search the database for your disease/condition and see who is doing the most studies on it. Or, find an article on your disease with the highest number of patients studied, as in "Study of 453 patients with muliple myeloma." That's a lot of patients. Now, google the top three doctors listed as authors of the study, find their medical center websites, and read their resumés. You have just found an expert on your disease/condition.

Are you really, really motivated to know all about your disease/condition? If you are one of the few, the brave, the persistent, you might want to take the next step. I found the twenty surgeons in the United States who had experience with my rare cancer and sent them all a letter. I printed the letter on the official business letterhead of my massage practice, which makes me look pretty darn professional myself.

If you are going to appeal to expert docs about your condition, make it a compelling story.

So . . . I sent out the following letter. It must have been engaging, because within days, my phone started ringing. Doctors were calling me, teaching me about this rare disease. Heads of medical schools were calling me. Surgeons were calling me, asking me to read them medical reports over the phone.

The "Expert Doctor" Letter

People, especially people who have just heard a dire diagnosis and are scared witless, can be awfully timid. Sort of like a deer in the headlights. They say, "How do I get my doctor to find an expert?" or "How do I get my doctor to approach the expert for me?" Short answer? Not gonna happen. Or if it does happen, it won't happen fast enough for you. Call them yourself, write them yourself. Become a professional; turn yourself into a colleague. And be sure, always, to tell a good story:

Dear Dr. So-and-so;

I found your name on a website dedicated to Pseudomyxoma Peritonei. My doctors seem to know slim-to-none about my condition—benign adenomucinosis:

> **Doctor #1,** before surgery: "It is most likely advanced ovarian cancer."

> **Surgeon #1,** after surgery and biopsy results: "It is not ovarian, and it is not cancer."

One day I have a dreaded diagnosis. Then massive surgery. Then, ten days later, I call my friends and family and tell them that the nightmare is over. Three weeks later I return to Surgeon #2 for the post-operative visit:

> **Surgeon #2:** "You have cancer. It has a 30% chance of recurring within five years."

Back to Surgeon #1 who told me that I didn't have cancer:

> **Surgeon #1:** "What you have is a Chronic Manageable Condition."

When I saw the oncologist for the first time, he gave the usual speech— what you have is so rare . . . we really don't know anything about it . . . etc. So I asked, "The cancer surgeon says that it has a 30% chance of recurring in five years. What do you think of that?"

> **Oncologist:** "You have two good years left."

Just like that. He went on about how they cut out all the cancer that they could see, but that undoubtedly there were lots of cancer cells left. All that we could do was wait around—for two years—and cut them out all over again.

I asked the oncologist, "Why do you keep saying two years? Why two years?" He said that, in the two patients whom he has seen in his thirty+ years of practice with pseudomyxoma, it came back after two years.

I am writing to ask you, who surely have seen more than two patients, is this so? Do people always need surgery again in two years?

Also, have you ever offered any further treatment options for this condition other than the Sugarbaker procedure?

Thank you so much for your help. I just needed to know a little more, as it is my life on the line.

Best regards,
Laurie Todd

Finally, you will find doctors who know something about your disease/condition, doctors who aren't trying to lull you into complacency, as in, "Let's just watch and wait." One of the surgeons laid it on the line to me: "Let me tell you what your life will be like if you do not get the Sugarbaker-type surgery and chemotherapy. The surgeries will come at lesser and lesser intervals—two years, one-and-a-half years, one year, six months. Each time they remove the recurring tumor, it will take more and more of your organs with it. Eventually, you will be in the nursing home with no stomach and no colon, feeding tube, permanent ostomy. Where will your HMO be then?"

Horrifying as this advice may sound, it was immensely comforting to me. Finally, the clean clear bracing air of truth. A patch of solid ground on which to take my stand.

An eminent pathologist called, asking me to read the operative report and pathology report over the phone, then said, "There is no way that anyone can tell you how long it will take for this to come back, unless they have done (And here he listed them.) all sorts of very expensive genetic tests of the tumor material. Which, I guarantee you, have not been done." I considered the ramifications: Dr. Two-Good-Years was wrong about the two good years. Head of Oncology at the HMO. Man, oh man.

One by one the sixteen experts checked in. A pattern was beginning to emerge . . . we do it like Sugarbaker, we learned it from Sugarbaker, we differ from Sugarbaker. Hey . . . I'm going to Sugarbaker!

Dr. Sugarbaker's office called. Ilse, his V.P. in charge of everything, explained a little more about the scary surgery and intraperitoneal chemotherapy, what tests they required before I could be considered for surgery, what challenges I could expect from the insurance company over the next few months.

We Seriously Afflicted develop a very short learning curve. Within the space of a few days, I went from believing that the Sugarbaker treatment was "ghastly and gruesome" to knowing, without a doubt, that this was exactly what I needed do.

Talk to the expert doctors yourself. Be respectful, be prepared. Do not pick up that phone until you have prepared your list of questions. Don't worry . . . they won't be dismissive or condescending. No tears, no hysterics—tell a compelling story and talk to them as though they were your respected colleagues. Ask your questions, interview them. You will be surprised how kind they will be, how willing to help. Call, listen, and TAKE NOTES!

CHAPTER 5

Grand Strategy:

Follow Your Healthcare Battle Plan

I have cancer, my local doctors are not interested, my health insurer will not pay for the only treatment which could save my life. My friends—both healthcare professionals and civilians—are of the opinion that I will never get my insurer to pay. What shall I do?

Then, along comes Jens. An acquaintance calls me, "There is someone you need to meet—my husband's cousin Jens Laundrup. Jens helped his wife get experimental treatment for her rare cancer after Blue Cross denied it . . . now he helps people in the same situation."

Finally, an ally. Not only did Jens secure the out-of-network "experimental" treatment for his wife, but he was also caregiver for his wife and three small children. Because of his work background, he was somewhat of an expert on bureaucracies. He was an extremely intelligent, no-nonsense, can-do type of guy. And funny . . . as I was to learn as I moved through my Insurance War, a little humor was grease for the wheels, food for the spirit, balm for the heart. When

47

*the whole nerve-wracking situation started to close in on me,
humor gave me some space.*

*Jens was my Insurance Warrior when I needed one most.
Of course, since we never know what we are in training for,
I didn't realize that he was modeling for me how to* BE *an
Insurance Warrior.*

*We spent several hours discussing strategy and tactics
for fighting the insurer. We also covered everything from
finances to nutrition to dealing with the government. I asked
questions, took six pages of notes, then had a good cry. Find
someone else to handle the bills, he said . . . this is too much
for you. I didn't have anyone else. So, I said, I will do it all
myself.*

*I'm a quick study; I came out of there prepared to become
the general, take command of my troops, and pursue a
fierce assault upon my enemy—those who would deny me
treatment.*

✳ ✳ ✳

Your mission is to get the treatment. As you become embroiled
in your Clash of the Titans with the insurance company, it is
critical that you stay focused on your objective. It's not about
money for YOU, and it's not about winning. It's about you
getting your lifesaving treatment. If you lose sight of this, you
are dead. Your heirs may win some money later on behalf of
your estate, but that is no use to you . . . you are dead.

The health insurer's mission is to control costs. The officers
in charge of cost-containment are the in-network doctors
who actually deal with you personally, the customer service
functionaries who talk to you, and the decision-making bean

counters behind the scenes. They are arrayed like a well-oiled military machine to hang onto those dollars.

You, on the other hand, are one person. You are a responsible citizen. You pay your premiums and expect to be respected. You follow the rules. You pay sticker price. How can you fight the health insurer? How can you ignore their threats? How can you go to your treatment if you do not yet have the insurer on board to pay for it?

During my Clash of the Titans with the HMO, I studied many lawsuits against health insurers—looking for angles and language to use in my appeal. I would like a dime for every case where it was the family of the insured, suing on behalf of his estate. He was dead. This is not good!

From now on, you are the general in charge of your battle to find and receive the best and most effective treatment for your condition/disease. Your in-network doctors may help you, they may ignore you, they may fight tooth and nail to deny you your lifesaving treatment. You appreciate any help that you receive from them, but you do not expect it. For you, getting this treatment is your number one objective.

All of this matters more to you than it does to the insurance company gatekeepers. It's like the chicken and the pig. When you order a bacon-and-egg breakfast, the chicken is involved and the pig is committed. Your health insurer is involved; you are committed.

In other words, nobody is more motivated to save your life than you. So, take the bull by the horns (or the pig by the tail) and make your physicians work with you—and for you. You are the general, they are the troops.

The Battle Plan

- Persuade an in-network doctor to request a referral for the out-of-network consult. If the doctor will not refer you—or the insurer will not pay for the consult, pay out-of-pocket and move on to Step Two.

- Go for the out-of-network consult, come home with a report/ treatment plan.

- Request the out-of-network ("experimental," "investigational," whatever they call it) treatment.

- Insurer denies payment for the treatment, or agrees to pay at the out-of-network rate.

- Write and submit your appeal.

You win the appeal, and you proceed to your treatment in peace. People always ask me, "What if I don't win the appeal?" I answer, "We have never lost a case. It may take two appeals; however, it is simply not that difficult to defeat the insurance company. They count on the desperately ill patients to just fold up their tents and give up. If you sound tough and you look troublesome, they will cave."

The HMO wars are just a chess game, a very high-stakes chess game. Let's say that you go bankrupt, lose your house and wind up sleeping on someone's couch but still get your treatment. They are sending you bills for $200,000. You have no money. SO WHAT? You can't squeeze a nickel and make the buffalo fart! You got the treatment, you are alive, that's all that matters.

The saddest case I encountered was the case of a man who had pancreatic cancer. He kept politely writing the HMO to ask for out-of-network treatment. He never escalated, never fought his way through the bureaucracy to find the decision-makers, never figured out how to spur them into action. He just kept writing his letters, begging and pleading for a response. The tone of the letters became increasingly desperate.

Finally, he died. Two weeks later, his widow received approval for the treatment. And she went on to sue the HMO on behalf of his estate. Is this what you are waiting for?

You are probably not a lawyer, nor are you a doctor. (Being a doctor may not be to your advantage anyhow; I have found that doctors in Bad Medical Trouble are often very reluctant to buck the system.) How are you to muster up the courage and the operational wherewithal to challenge an entire army?

The best description of how we little individuals win these big victories comes from one of my helpees. He said, "As a former prize-fighter, I know that a bluff-down is as good as a knock-down."

We are not planning to sue our insurance companies. We just have to demonstrate to them that we would, if we wanted to sue them, have an excellent case. We are not lawyers, but I will show you how to sound like a lawyer. An invincible lawyer, the finest lawyer that money can buy. A lawyer who is as tough as nails. It is enough . . . a bluff-down is as good as a knock-down.

You will turn yourself into a professional soldier—the general, in fact. The guiding principles of your Grand Strategy:

- **Never take anything personally**

  This is war.

  Yes, I know that you are fighting for your life. You are sick, you have been paying for your health insurance for twenty years, and suddenly you discover that they don't want to pay for your lifesaving treatment. It is bad, Really Bad. It's not fair; it's unjust. Have a major rant-and-rave session, then get over it. It is nothing personal. It is simply their job not to pay for your treatment, and it is your job to make them pay.

  Let your friends and family sit around and discuss how unfair it all is. You need to throw everything you have at your decisive objective; you have no energy left over for bemoaning or complaining.

- **Be smarter than they are**

  As you will see, an insurance company is a giant bureaucracy. All of the health insurers use the same obstructionist strategies every time, in the same order. Once you learn what their tactics are and how to counter them, you will be one step ahead of them.

  Besides, you have the advantage of flexibility. Your army is light and lean and can maneuver. You can change your tactics at the drop of a hat. The insurer, however, always has to proceed through the same sluggish channels in the same ways.

  One day recently the phone rang, "You don't know me . . . my name is Robin. I printed off all of your posts on the

Bellybuttons group and put them in a binder." She went on to explain that she had persuaded the insurer to pay for her husband's out-of-network treatment. Robin was my all-time star helpee . . . she won the battle all on her own, with no college degree, no special training. All she had was bits of my advice from an on-line rare cancer forum and an invincible spirit. You have the entire plan and all the weapons; it will be much easier for you.

- Maintain momentum until success is accomplished

From now on, doing battle with the health insurer is your full-time job.

CHAPTER 6

Prepare for Battle:

Do Your Research

To do battle, you must first arm yourself.

First, put on your armor of dispassionate professionalism. Yes, I know that you are fighting for your life, they are trying to kill you, it's not fair. All the more reason to keep a cool head and fight them with their own language and in ways that they can understand. Believe me, your insurer—and the insurance doctors associated with them—have heard every pitiful sob-story in the book. Yours is just one more number on a spreadsheet to them.

Second, have compassion for your opponent—for two reasons. It is by understanding your opponent's strategy that you gain the advantage in any game. Also, being sensitive to your insurance opponent's concerns and wishing to alleviate them will give you some powerful practice in opening your heart.

Open your heart to all of them: local docs who would discourage you from having any treatment, government bureaucrats who would have you reduced to the homeless shelter, friends and acquaintances who have a million reasons why they could never get cancer. The more you embrace the whole experience, the sooner you will win the right battles and leave the useless ones behind.

Now that you have your strategic philosophical underpinnings in place, on to the instruction manual for winning your own Clash of the Titans:

• Get some official-looking stationery

    . . . you will need it for months and years to come. If you have letters after your name, use them all. Design a clean, tasteful letterhead with all your contact information including e-mail address and fax number, if you have one.

• Buy a file box

    . . . or dedicate a file drawer to your illness/injury. Buy a box of manilla file folders and a package of file folder labels.

• Study your insurance policy

    If I were a malpractice lawyer, the first thing that I would tell you to do is to pore over every page of your health insurance policy. Study especially the definition of "medical necessity." There are many medical/legal terms that, when used, can spur the insurer into action. This is the most important one. Study also all provisions pertaining to out-of-network care.

• Order your complete medical record and read it

    . . . you will find plenty of ammo in there for your appeal, and you will read things in there which will curl your hair! If you read all of the doctors' notes for each visit, you will undoubtedly find a slip-up, a casual comment—the nugget of gold that will bolster your case. Remember, the insurer has to stand by what its own agents—your doctors—say.

One of my local surgeons wrote, "I advised her to seek a second opinion." Say what? Solid gold.

- Dedicate a notebook to your conversations with the insurance company

  Whenever you call, note the day and time, what you discussed, and the name of the person to whom you spoke. The "who" is the most important part, as it is your proof that the conversation actually took place. One of these bureaucrats is bound to slip up and say something that will strengthen your case. All of this documentation will become ammo for your appeal, should you need to make one. Even if there are no gold nuggets in your conversations with the insurance company, the fact that you kept such meticulous records will scare the livin' daylights out of them.

- Listen to—and write down—everything that the doctor or the bureaucrats at the insurance company say to you

  You are like primitive man in the forest—noticing everything, using all your senses. You are always thinking "tactics"; you are always looking for angles to work, and you are always looking for leverage.

- Seek out a "double agent"

  If you get really shrewd and really lucky, you may even find a double agent within the organization who can reveal some of the hidden strategies to you and help you on your way. As you talk to dozens of different functionaries and bean counters at the insurance company, listen for that morsel of help, that tone of compassion. Keep that person on the phone, bond with them, milk them for all the help you can get.

  When this person steps out of their bureaucratic role to help you, thank them. Write a letter to their supervisor/manager singing their praises. Always be mindful, however, that they work for your opponent, the insurance company. They can only go so far to help you, and you must be careful not to blow their cover.

- Hit the internet big-time

  You are seriously going to google. Google your disease/condition, google your doctors, google your health insurer. For example, if your health insurer is Acme Health, search for "Acme Health," "sue Acme Health," "make Acme Health pay" . . . you will learn how other people have dealt with the insurer, find phrases and language that you can use.

  If you have no computer skills, have a friend or family member do the computer work for you. If nobody has a computer, reserve a computer at your local library every day. If there are no computers at your local library, make very good friends with the reference librarian and ask him/her to search for you.

- Find a forum for your disease/condition

You want a forum with a message board or chat group. Here you will find your allies, your fellow soldiers . . . these folks are on your side, and they are eager to help you. You will be able to read about others' experience with the treatment which you are considering. You will also find practical tips about how to prepare for your treatment, and how to take best care of yourself afterward.

Be sure, however, to take the opinions of your fellow sufferers with a gigantic grain of salt. People will espouse certain treatment plans, medications, "natural" cures. They will be fiercely loyal to their physicians of choice. Lists of doctors on websites or forums are just lists. . . . Moses did not receive these lists on the mountaintop. You do not know if these doctors have been vetted or qualified. Take the information, then do your own research. You want to look for doctors and treatments which yield consistent good results.

Do your homework. I have seen people blindly follow the recommendations given on groups or websites, only to wind up in serious medical jeopardy.

Most importantly for your insurance war—you may be able to put out a call and find people with your same insurer who have already had this treatment and gotten it paid for. That's precedent, people! Precedent is some of the most powerful ammo that you can find for your appeal. It's a contract, they provided this service already to another contract-holder just like you. They paid for it before, they have to pay for it now.

- Call a lawyer and get free advice

  I phoned a lawyer who turned out to be talkative . . . kept him on the phone for a half-hour, getting free advice. Your town may have a free legal advice clinic; call your local Bar Association. Or, contact the Patient Advocate Foundation— lawyers are there, ready to advise you pro bono.

- Make friends with your Insurance Commissioner

  Every state has an Office of the Insurance Commissioner. (The title may vary from state to state, but the duties are the same.) Among its other functions, the Office of the Insurance Commissioner is there to advocate for you with your insurance company. Just google "insurance commissioner ohio (or whatever state applies)." Write down the phone number, and make note of how to file a grievance, should you need to do so.

  Insurance Commissioners have put pressure on health insurers to pay for treatment—usually at the eleventh hour, as the insured is being wheeled into surgery. When the insurer stonewalls you, refusing to tell you who their decision-makers are, the Insurance Commissioner can sometimes supply names and phone numbers. If the insurer isn't abiding by the time limits or guidelines which apply to appeals, you can file a complaint with the Insurance Commissioner.

  Call the Insurance Commissioner's office for advice every step of the way: "Can they do this? How do I proceed with that?"

And be sure, always, to copy ("cc") the Insurance Commissioner by name at the bottom of every letter to your insurer. It puts them on notice that you know the Insurance Commissioner, and you know how to use him!

- Become familiar with www.appeallettersonline.com

  They have all sorts of free newsletter articles chock full of insider information on how to appeal billing and denial of care decisions. Grab a few phrases from one of these articles, and you will sound like a billing and coding expert!

Don't listen to all the doom-sayers who believe that it is impossible to press your own case against the insurer. The folks at the insurance company are bureaucrats; they always use the same tactics in the same order every time. You are smarter than they are; it is a battle of wits with an unarmed opponent!

CHAPTER 7

Intelligence:

Know Your Insurance Opponent

When we embark upon the health insurance part of our high-stakes battle, we patients are at a terrible disadvantage. We have no idea what the rules of engagement are. What are our doctors basing their advice on, what pressures influence their decisions, what constraints are placed on them? We are not privy to all of the insurance-provider doctors' concerns and objections. I don't have to be . . . all I really need to know is "follow the money."

In earlier times (before the 1970s), the doctor was a check and balance on the insurance company. The doctor knew you, followed the progress of your case, and assisted you in getting whatever care you needed in order to get better. The doctor was the "general" of your army, overseeing your case, commanding the troops, and battling the insurer on your behalf.

The insurance company operated on the premise that you paid your premiums for many years, and they needed to pay for your care—within reason. If the insurer didn't want to pay, and you needed a test or a medication or a treatment to save your life, your doctor would go to bat for you.

Times have changed. During the late 1960s, health insurers became acutely aware that healthcare costs were sky-rocketing. In their infinite wisdom, the actuaries and bean counters came up with the concept of "managed care."

Remember George Orwell's book *1984*? In his futuristic totalitarian state, everything is named the opposite of what it really is . . . double-speak. For example, the "Ministry of Truth" is in charge of lies and blatant propaganda. The wonderful world of insurance works the same way. Let's start with the word "managed care." The expression sounds vaguely benevolent, as though the insurer has somehow corralled the care, but is still dishing it out in abundance. Not so. Managed care means "managed costs." And, in order to manage costs, care is limited and/or denied. The health insurers have perfected a hundred different ways of making it appear as though you have coverage, then denying the care.

The most appalling irony of managed care is that healthcare costs have continued to sky-rocket. Medical care that cost $1 million dollars in 1970 would cost $18 million today. Patients have suffered and died as a result of denial of care, and it has failed miserably even as a business strategy.

Let's move on to the term "Primary Care Physician" . . . this title makes him sound like a powerful decision-maker (primary) who is there to provide "care." Not necessarily.

Look up "gatekeeper" in your Webster's dictionary: "A person who controls access." Then, look up "gatekeeper" in any insurance glossary: "A term applied to the primary care physician." Before your in-network doctor recommends any treatment, he must run it through his mental data-bank to see if the insurer will pay for it . . . he is the gatekeeper. My oncologist said to me, "There is no treatment for your disease. And, even if there were, they wouldn't pay for it." Remember, he is the gatekeeper. He knew that I needed care . . . this care was not available in the network. For whatever reasons, he was not planning to go out of his way to help me get it. The physician at your HMO or in your PPO network is employed by the insurance company. The insurance company generates his paycheck and determines his bonuses. Plus, they can terminate his contract. No more checks and balances. Insurance in charge, insurance gone wild.

Furthermore, the health insurers have gradually been changing their way of doing business over the last thirty-five years. Whereas before there was a good faith effort on their part to take care of our medical needs, now there seems to be an underlying principle of "heck no, we won't pay." And, if you make us pay, we won't pay much.

Don't get me wrong . . . I have a tremendous amount of compassion for the insurance companies. Hey, it is not easy to be a health insurer these days. These cutting-edge treatments for modern diseases are astronomically expensive. If every patient with cancer got the most up-to-date lifesaving treatments, the insurer would go broke . . . maybe. Or at least they seem to be operating under this assumption.

Managed care—is it a sustainable business model? It is as if the insurance company were a store, with all sorts of merchandise to offer (medical treatments). However, if everybody who wanted that merchandise came in and bought all of it, the store would go bankrupt. Modern medicine is very,

very expensive; hence, all of the underhanded attempts to get us oh-so-costly cancer people to cease and desist. The very best outcome from the insurance company perspective is that we die, and do so quickly.

Health insurance is no insurance against financial ruin. Seven out of ten people who suffer financial ruin for medical reasons have health insurance.[1] In other words, you may be safer financially WITHOUT health insurance than with it. Which would be bad enough, except that bankruptcy for medical reasons was recently outlawed. Shocking, isn't it?

As you embark upon your own Insurance Wars, it behooves you to know how insurance companies operate—in general. It is also a wise idea to know as much about your own insurer as possible.

Your health insurer

The internet will be your best friend in learning about your health insurer. I studied my HMO's website closely, reading the history of the organization, their guiding principles, etc. First, I discovered that my HMO was formed back in 1970 as a sort of socially responsible, hippy-commune of an HMO, with its purpose to provide affordable healthcare to the masses. Good news . . . perhaps there remained a vestige of humanitarian spirit in this outfit.

Second, I learned that my HMO had a loose affiliation with the HMO giant of the West, Kaiser. My HMO shared "best clinical practices" with Kaiser. I couldn't find many lawsuits against my HMO, small and relatively polite as they were. I probably

1 From "I Can't Afford to Get Sick!" *Reader's Digest*, April 2006.

wouldn't be able to dig up a member of my small HMO with my rare cancer, who had pursued out-of-network treatment, and who had gotten it paid for (precedent). However, there was a wealth of litigation and precedent about Kaiser. Major pay dirt.

Your health insurer probably offers an organizational chart somewhere on their website. Print it and keep it in your files . . . you may need to contact these bigwigs.

You will also gather information about your health insurer as you wrangle with them on the phone and by mail. Who reports to whom? Who are the decision-makers? Grab all of the phone numbers and email addresses that you can. You are going to be engaging in a war of exhaustion with these people— pestering them ceaselessly until they roll over and cry uncle.

I have found that different types of insurers require different approaches. The grand strategy is the same: I will sue the livin' pants off of you if you don't pay for my treatment. However, the tactics do differ.

HMOs

HMOs get a pretty bad rap out there in the patient world. I am a longtime HMO member—two different HMOs, two different states. You will never get OVER-treated at an HMO . . . these providers do not want to see you darken their door unless absolutely necessary. Since I do not aspire to become a perpetual patient, this is A-OK with me.

I have found, contrary to all accepted urban legends, that HMOs are the easiest to make pay. If you have a major out-of-network cancer treatment on your horizon, thank your lucky stars if you have an HMO. They are a one-entity organization, they present a fixed target. Who knows, they may retain a vestige of the humanitarian principles by which they were founded. They really don't want bad press and lawsuits out there; they will cave in faster than any other type of health insurer. I thought that I had the worst, funkiest HMO insurance West of the Rockies, but they paid every penny for my out-of-network treatment.

PPOs

I include all of the big insurance boys in this category. The heavy hitters . . . you know who they are. Some of these health insurers are bigger than others. The bigger they are, the harder they are to fight. The ones who offer the most expensive, "cadillac of insurances," are the hardest of all to make pay. They are so expert at not paying that their very organization throws up major roadblocks.

The biggest insurer has split off into scores of different entities: "Acme of Ohio," "Independence Acme," "Acme Lonestar," "Acme of California." Try to find precedent. You will have to find someone within your particular branch of the insurance company who has had the same treatment for the same thing and had it paid for. I've done it, but it's not easy. Try to find the decision-maker who can agree to a single-case contract with your out-of-network doctor. Bring your pot of coffee to the phone and settle in for a long siege.

Medicare

Medicare is its own illusion of coverage. On average, they pay about 7% of certain complex surgeries. THAT'S SEVEN PERCENT,

PEOPLE. "But I have supplemental insurance," you say. Ah, there's that double-speak again. "Supplemental" . . . sounds like they pay . . . well . . . the rest. Wrong. Whereas Medicare pays around seven percent for complex services, your supplemental insurance pays about 2%. You are paying for an insurance that pays nearly nothing. Between the two of them, your physician may see ten percent of his billed charges. The amount that Medicare pays is based on what they call "AMA Guidelines." Sounds official, doesn't it? Well, if you dig deeply enough, you will find that these AMA Guidelines are private. That means that patients and providers are not informed of what they are; and they CHANGE MONTHLY, depending on what procedures are popular that month. They will certainly want to pay less for them, so as to improve the profits for that month.

When I tried to find a doctor to care for my mother, I found only one practicing physician in a large urban area who would accept her. One can only imagine what sort of social havoc will ensue once we baby boomers start hitting Medicare like a tsunami.

Once Medicare denies a service, the enrollee has sixty days to appeal that determination; the Medicare+Choice plan must re-evaluate the decision within thirty days, if that decision involves denial of care. If Medicare upholds its initial decision, the case moves on to the Center for Health Dispute Resolution (CHDR), an independent contractor that reconsiders appeals. The CHDR can take anywhere from seventy-two hours (for life-threatening situations) to thirty days to render a decision.

If the CHDR decides against the patient, he may take his case to the Administrative Law Judge (ALJ). If the ALJ decides unfavorably, the patient can proceed on to the Departmental Appeals Board (DAB). The DAB can take up to a year to come to a decision. IF YOU AREN'T DEAD BY THEN! Sound incredibly cumbersome? Sound like alphabet soup? Sound like a mountain of red tape for a sick, tired senior citizen? If you can't wrap your mind around this process, visit www.medicarerights.org for more information.

Medicare is very "appeal-able." If you can persist through the mountain of red tape, they often reverse their determinations. In other words, you can get them to pay, but they won't pay much.

Military Insurance (TriCare)

The reimbursement rate for TriCare is tied to the reimbursement rate for Medicare. Right . . . around 7%. If you are covered by TriCare, you are welcome to go to any doctor you choose. GOOD LUCK FINDING A CIVILIAN DOCTOR WHO WANTS TO WORK FOR 7%!

An appeal works because we have the option of suing the insurer. We are not GOING to sue them; we just imply that we would have a really, really good case. So . . . can we sue military insurance? The happy answer is "yes." We cannot sue them if we are active military, but we can sue them if we are retired.

TriCare is a federal program, so it is not governed by state insurance laws, nor is it regulated or overseen by an Insurance Commissioner. If you can't get anywhere with your case manager, your best path to a successful conclusion is through your senator or congressman—whoever you think might be more sympathetic to the plight of our military men and women.

What you will need to do is write a "white paper." A white paper is identical to an appeal, just directed to an audience of one—your political representative. In this white paper, you will present all of the facts that prove that TriCare needs to pay for your proposed treatment. Include attachments to prove your point, just as you would do in an appeal. Do all the work, because your senator's staff is not going to lift a finger or do anything extra for you. You need to give them all the ammunition they need to win the case and look like heroes. Then, stand back and let them go to bat for you.

Learn to speak their language

You don't need to be fluent in "insurance-speak" in order to win the Insurance War. You just need to understand what your insurer means by "medically necessary," "usual and customary," and "accepted medical standards."

- Medically necessary

   I often ask my helpees, "What does the phrase "medically necessary" mean? They answer, "Necessary to maintain my health," "necessary to treat my disease," "necessary to save my life." WRONG!

   The words "medically necessary" are pure medical legalese—they mean nothing. And everything. When you sign up with the health insurer, you state, in effect: "Medical necessity means whatever my health insurer says it means." Scary, isn't it?

- Accepted medical standards

  So . . . you go to the Definitions section of your benefits booklet, and you look up "medically necessary." You will find a long, convoluted definition with all sorts of twists and turns. You press on, and you come to the phrase, "according to accepted medical standards." Since I question everything, I wondered, "What are these 'accepted medical standards'?" I searched through state statutes pertaining to healthcare, I corresponded with medical associations, I called the reference librarian at the library. Guess what? THERE ARE NO SUCH THINGS AS ACCEPTED MEDICAL STANDARDS! It's all smoke and mirrors.

- Usual and customary

  When the health insurer finally agrees to pay for your out-of-network, "experimental" or "investigational" treatment, they will use the phrase "usual and customary" to try to limit their payment. We will pay, but only the amount that WE deem to be "usual and customary."

  Once again, what does "usual and customary" mean? It means whatever your health insurer says it means. Your health insurer has either a computerized list of fees attached to certain codes, or they will state that they follow "AMA Guidelines" in determining how much to pay. As we have learned, these AMA Guidelines are confidential (You are not privy to them.) and constantly changing, according to the insurance company's bottom line.

• Bundling and deletion of codes

Code bundling is another way that the insurers have of reducing reimbursement for medical services. They agree to pay your expert surgeon—who does not participate in their network—for an intricate thirteen-hour abdominal surgery. The surgeon's usual charge for this surgery is $15,000. They simply lump this procedure in with a few others, according to their "guidelines," then pay their "usual and customary" fee for a hernia repair—$1,500. Depending on the wording of your policy, the surgeon who just saved your life gets paid peanuts. Or, if the surgeon is allowed to balance-bill, he turns around and bills YOU for $13,500. Surprise!

Every word of this circular logic is meant to put all of the power firmly in the hands of the insurer. However, the definitions are so vague that you can turn them to your advantage. Let's look at my HMO's definition of "Medical Necessity" and see how this works:

Medically Necessary: Appropriate and clinically necessary services, as determined by the HMO's Medical Director, or his/her designee, according to generally accepted principles of good medical practice, which are rendered to a Member for the diagnosis, care or treatment of a Medical Condition. Services must be medically and clinically necessary for benefits to be covered under the Agreement. In order to be Medically Necessary, services must meet the following requirements: a) are not solely for the convenience of the Member; b) are the most appropriate level of service or supply which can be safely provided to the Member; c) are for the diagnosis or treatment of an actual Medical Condition; d) are not for life-enhancing or palliative therapy, except for terminal conditions; e) are appropriate and consistent with the diagnosis and which, in accordance with accepted medical standards in the State of Anystate; f) are not experimental or investigational.

There you have it . . . a ton of convoluted legalese designed to intimidate and deter. The Medical Director of the insurance company gets to decide what is "medically necessary" for me. In other words, with this definition, I have granted my health insurer nearly divine powers.

I turned this load of verbiage to my advantage by proving, in my appeal, that cyto-reductive surgery plus heated intra-peritoneal chemotherapy IS the accepted standard of care by the National Organization of Rare Disorders and Blue Cross of California. I pointed out to them that Kaiser, their "partner in best clinical practices," routinely paid for this out-of-network treatment for my same rare cancer. I included "peer-reviewed" (the highest standard for published papers) studies and papers showing that my expert surgeon had done this procedure over nine hundred times, with proven good outcomes; thus, it was not experimental/investigational. I knew that I didn't have to measure my chosen treatment against "accepted medical standards" in my state, because no such standards exist.

Cover all the points listed in their definition of medical necessity. Prove that your proposed treatment meets all of the important conditions and ignore the ones that are just hot air.

CHAPTER 8

Tactics:

Counter Their Objections

I have muddled my way through conflicting diagnoses and prognoses. I have dipped my toe into the Internet, and I suspect that there may be curative treatment for my disease.

Armed with this information, I head off to my first appointment with the oncologist. Now, mind you, I have never met this man before. He walks into the room, looking for all the world like a rumpled, slightly weary sixty-year-old junior high school teacher. He greets me, saying that my cancer is so rare, nobody knows anything about it. Right . . . and I am supposed to believe what you say about it? I say, "Dr. Jones told me that I had a 30% chance of recurrence in five years . . . what do you think of that?" He says, "You have two good years left." Just like that.

I was learning, but I was still a tender soul—yet again my face went white. "That is really bad news," I say. "Yes, it is," he replies with a smile.

He goes on to tell me what the next two years will look like. The doctors at the HMO will keep draining fluid out of me as the cancer recurs, doing repeated surgeries as it fills my abdomen. By now, I am feisty enough—even in the face of these gruesome prognostications about my future, to question his assumptions. "You keep saying 'two years'. Why two years? Based on what?" "In my career, I have treated two patients with this disease, and it took two years before they needed surgery again." Two patients. Two patients were enough for him to make predictions about the length of my life? I smiled. I nodded. I kept my cool.

Mind you, I am sure that this doctor is a wonderful oncologist when handling the more common cancers. You have breast cancer? Big smile, dish out the appropriate dose of radiation and chemotherapy. It's just that, in my case, he did everything in his power to make sure that I would receive only palliative treatment for my cancer. Based on the experiences of two patients. So, I have come to refer to him as "Dr. Two-Good-Years."

Thanks to Dr. Two-Good-Years," I would never approach a doctor's appointment the same way again.

I was shocked that Dr. TGY knew so little about my cancer and didn't seem at all interested in learning anything about it. Since then, I have learned that many cancer patients have had a similar experience. They are usually not offered palliative care only, as I was. More often, people with rare or unusual cancers are offered chemotherapy, whether it has been shown to be effective for their cancer or not.

Have appendix cancer? How about a "colon cancer protocol?" Appendix cancer does not behave in any way like colon cancer, and the course of chemotherapy for colon cancer may be useless, of some use, useful, or may drastically reduce the chance of a good outcome. Who is going to decide whether you should go through it or not? You.

It feels to me as though there exists somewhere a "laundry list" of cancer treatments. You get a certain combination of surgery, chemotherapy and radiation for this cancer, you get another combination for that cancer. If your cancer doesn't appear on the list, too bad for you. Makes one wonder . . . who decides what cancer treatments will be offered by a health insurer? What are their criteria for determining that these protocols are safe and effective? Do they ever revise their offerings, and what would it take for them to revise them?

It is as if you walked into a store and asked for socks. The salesperson hands you underpants. You say, "I don't want underpants . . . I asked for socks!" The sales clerk says, "Underpants are what we have today, and underpants are what you get."

If you have one of the more popular cancers, this approach may be, well . . . not great, but OK. If you have a rare or difficult cancer which does not act like other cancers, this approach could destroy you, with no effect on the cancer at all. As soon as you ask to be referred out of network, expect a torrent of objections. You may find an in-network doctor who is willing and eager to refer you, but don't count on it. Besides the cost-containment factor, the doctor may be subjected to a host of pressures that you know nothing about.

I cannot speak to why your doctor may not refer you out of network. I did, however, sit across from Dr. Two-Good-Years and listen to him explain why I would receive only palliative care. My sense was that he saw more work and more headache ahead if he referred me out. He didn't want to waste his effort, telling me, "They will just say 'no'." He may have assumed that I was the typical helpless patient; I would pester him constantly, and he would have to do all of the work of the appeal for me. Perhaps this had happened to him in the past.

Perhaps his ego prevented him from referring me. He may have been the type of person who does not want to admit that anyone knows more than he does. He may be a controlling type of person, saying "no" just because he will not tolerate any resistance to his program. Or, worst of all, he may receive a bonus for limiting my access to the care which I needed, or a sanction of some type for helping me to access that care.

I have even heard of network doctors being fined or reprimanded for referring patients out of network. Your doctor may have many reasons not to send you to an expert. Hey, I wouldn't be surprised if one of these doctors said, "I wouldn't send my mother to Dr. Expert. Dr. Expert will do a voodoo dance, insult your ancestors, and pull your giblets out through your nose."

Six months after I had gotten my treatment from an expert surgeon and moved on, I received a form letter from Dr. TGY's office, stating that he was cutting down his hours in anticipation of retirement. Who knows . . . perhaps he was just tired, worn down by a lifetime of treating cancer patients. Suffice it to say, I needed to assess the situation and realize that he was not the oncologist for me.

Fortunately, Dr. TGY didn't offer me colon cancer treat-

ment, or I might have taken it. Instead, he offered me no treatment at all, which offended me mightily, and awoke the sleeping Insurance Warrior within. Starting the next day, I launched a massive campaign to secure the best treatment available anywhere in the United States.

* * *

People wrangling with their health insurers ask me, "Why did my doctor do this? Why did my doctor say that?" We will never know. However, I have found that many doctors will make a strong case for whatever treatments are available in the network, or contracted with the insurer.

I have learned that the series of hoops that Dr. TGY put me through are standard for a doctor who is working under the auspices of an insurance company. And, be it an HMO (provides discounted services through a limited network of doctors and hospitals) or a PPO (provides services through a loose network of doctors who provide services for a discounted fee), your doctor, when he makes his recommendations, may have to consider whether the insurer will pay for them. I am not saying that your doctor does not have your best medical interests at heart . . . he may. I am just saying that it behooves you to discover whether decisions on what tests, treatments, surgeries you undergo are based on best current medical wisdom or on cost containment.

If it is the latter, and you are determined to receive care that your insurer does not want to pay for, you must make your way through the Cost-Containment Obstacle Course. It is really quite easy to make your way successfully through these roadblocks, as the insurers always deploy their tactics in exactly the same way and exactly the same order.

Following are some of the standard tactics of your opponent, the health insurer.

- Offer no treatment

  That's the "watchful waiting" scenario. It has its own seductive appeal . . . no surgery, no chemo—I don't have to face anything scary right away. And it may actually BE the best course for some people with some illnesses/conditions. Just make darned sure that it is, because, for the Seriously Afflicted, there are no do-overs.

  In my case, had I gone with the "watchful waiting" scenario, my cancer would soon have been so advanced and done such damage to my digestive system that I would soon have had no chance of a good outcome. It would have been a terrible way to go, a death sentence.

  Your tactic: If your doctor prescribes "watchful waiting," read every study and interview every doctor you can find in order to discover whether this approach makes sense in your case.

- Refer you to a local doctor who is contracted with the insurance company

  He is contracted with them . . . as the gatekeeper, your doctor needs to send you to them first. There is nothing wrong with this. Just make darned sure that he is qualified and experienced, not just affordable.

Your tactic: Interview the local doctor yourself. Ask him the qualifying questions yourself (How many patients with this disease are you currently treating? How many of these procedures have you done? What are your outcomes?). Write down his answers word-for-word . . . you may be quoting him in your appeal.

Also, google this local doctor and find his medical center website. Print his bio and keep it in your files. If the bio shows that he has no experience nor interest in your disease/condition, no training in it, and terrible outcomes, you will use his bio as ammo in your appeal.

- **Scare them away from the out-of-network expert**

I have by now heard dozens of these scare tactics; they range from the absurd to the ridiculous. Why are local HMO/PPO doctors, primary care physicians, etc. so vehemently opposed to out-of-network experts? Why do they warn us against them so strongly, often without knowing anything about them? I will never understand it.

Dr. TGY said, "There is a guy named Sugarbaker, but you wouldn't want to go to him." "How come?" I asked. "Because, if you went to see him, you would be disabled." Disabled. Having already read quite a bit about Dr. Sugarbaker and his outcomes, I was bemused by this remark.

However, as I have met many insurance veterans since then, I have learned that it pales in comparison to some of the whoppers which are told to keep us in network. You wouldn't want to see an expert because. . . .

"Dr. Expert will take out all your organs."

The truth is that he is a master at saving organs . . . and lives.

"Doctor Expert skews his results."

So??? I'm not a statistician . . . I couldn't care less. Besides, what evidence do you have of this?

"Doctor Expert always does an ostomy (removes your ears, takes out your stomach . . . fill in the blank)."

Only if you need one for a safe and successful outcome.

"Doctor Expert will take out your rectum."

Only if you have cancer in it.

Besides, you do not need to be dissuaded by this. If you do the research, you will learn that the rectum is just the last portion of the intestine. You can live very happily and digest and eliminate just fine without it. And, if the rectum is cancerous, do you want your surgeon to leave it in? Some do, but that needs to be a decision informed by facts, not scare tactics.

"Doctor Expert is so busy . . . he won't be able to see you for months."

Call him yourself. One of my helpees was told this by her local doctor, only to call him herself and get an appointment three weeks later.

And my all-time favorite. . . .

"Since Dr. Expert is a brain surgeon, he always finds a brain tumor."

Say what? Does a cardiac surgeon always find a stenosed cardiac artery, just because that is his specialty? How does this guy know what the expert always does? Do these bean counters think we just fell off the turnip truck to fall for these scare tactics?

Your tactic: Inform yourself completely about the out-of-network doctor whom you have chosen. Qualify him by interviewing him or his staff, read his bio. Find the papers and studies that he has published and READ them. (If he is a major expert, he may have published some papers.) Talk to several other experts, to see what THEY have to say about your expert's approach. (Not about him personally . . . doctors do not want to comment about other doctors.) In other words, become an expert on your expert. Then, when your Primary Care Physician or local all-purpose oncologist starts telling these tall tales, you can smile, nod, and think about what you will be writing later in order to persuade him to refer you for your out-of-network treatment.

• **Deny payment for out-of-network treatment**

Your benefits booklet, which is a legal and binding contract, states that your insurer doesn't have to pay for out-of-network treatment unless it is emergency treatment. If you have a PPO or POS (Point of Service) agreement, you have an out-of-network benefit, which means that they will pay anywhere from 60%–80% of the in-network rate. This so-called benefit is just about useless, as far as I am concerned. Try paying 20% of a bone marrow transplant. You will be just as broke as you would be if you paid 100% of it. If you need out-of-network treatment for your life-threatening disease/condition, you will have to fight this out-of-network payment idea just as hard as you would fight a denial of care.

Your insurer will be happy to order up a second opinion for you, as long as it is by an in-network doctor who agrees with the first one.

Your tactic: Ignore the contract. If you have a life-threatening condition/disease, your insurer has to provide curative treatment for you. If there is no doctor in the network QUALIFIED to TREAT your disease, they have to send you out of network for treatment. You may refer to this as the "gap exception" . . . it will make you sound like an insider. All you will have to do is prove to them that none of the doctors in the network has sufficient knowledge or experience to successfully treat your disease.

- Deny payment, calling the treatment "experimental" or "investigational"

Remember, your insurer is not calling the treatment "experimental" because it IS experimental. They are calling it experimental, because they don't want to pay for it. They have no proof that the treatment is experimental. How could you prove such a thing? "Experimental" is one of those words like "medically necessary" or "usual and customary."

They mean nothing except whatever the insurer defines them to mean, and the insurer has no proof to back them up.

Furthermore, if your treatment were experimental, you would be required to sign a special release form; your doctor would have to notify you that you were going to be part of a study. Rest assured, your surgery/treatment/medication is probably not experimental. And, even if it is, there are still ways to make them pay for it.

Your tactic: Find the perfect peer-reviewed studies in the scholarly journals to prove that your expert doctor of choice has been administering this treatment to hundreds of patients for over twenty years with excellent, documented results. If you aren't computer-savvy enough to search through the studies on PubMed on the NIH website, find a friend to do it for you. If you do not have such a friend, call up the expert doctor whom you have chosen and ask him to send you some of his best studies.

• **Deny payment, claiming that the treatment is "not medically necessary"**

Are you getting the hang of this now? "Not medically necessary" means that they don't want to pay for it.

Your tactic: Look up the definition of "medically necessary" in your benefits booklet. Pull it apart and use it to prove your point. And, just in case they might persist with this objection, prove to them that all of the patients with your disease who have NOT had this treatment died, or had terrible outcomes. Prove that 70% of all patients who did have the treatment are still kicking around fifteen years later. Inundate them with facts. Not medically necessary? They will not be able defend that unfounded remark on ANY grounds once you get through with them.

- **Agree to pay, but only at the out-of-network rate**

The out-of-network rate will most likely be 60% to 80% of the in-network rate. Technically, this is not a denial. However, I would fight it just as vigorously as I would a denial. If your proposed treatment costs over $100,000, you will go just as broke paying 20% of it as you would paying 100% of it.

Your tactic: This is your "gap exception." You fight this the same way as you would a denial: If no doctor in the network is qualified to offer curative treatment for your life-threatening disease, then they need to send you to the doctor who IS qualified to treat you, and pay him the in-network rate.

- **Agree to pay, then, after the fact, find a dozen ways to pay only pennies on the dollar**

We will address this tactic in CHAPTER 10, "Resistance: *Make Them Pay It All.*"

CHAPTER 9

Diplomacy

Secure the Referral

When we last left my story, I had just been to see the ever cheerful Dr. TGY. He had informed me that, if I went for treatment by Dr. Sugarbaker, I would be disabled. He also mentioned a study of my proposed treatment by Sloan-Kettering where "everybody died." He offered: "Why don't we wait three months and see how fast it grows?" Finally, he said, "There is a local surgeon who is doing something like Sugarbaker." By now, I recognized that he was making the next move in the chess game: Suggest "watchful waiting," discourage the patient from seeing the expert, then . . . refer the patient to the local doctor who is contracted with the health insurer.

I asked, "You are a busy man. . . . How about if I interview the local doctor and report back to you?" He happily agreed, and I went off to read the studies in the Annals of Surgical Oncology, *interview the local surgeon, and prepare my talking points. I would have to convince Dr. TGY that it was his idea to refer me to Dr. Sugarbaker.*

* * *

The first hoop that you will need to jump through is the request for a referral for the out-of-network consult—the second opinion. The request for the treatment will come later. It will be very difficult to get your out-of-network treatment paid for if you don't have the referral from the in-network doctor. It can be done, but it is an uphill battle. Much easier to do the hard work up front and just get the referral. The referral is your "foot in the door."

The referral for the out-of-network consultation is a statement by the in-network doctor—the gatekeeper for the insurance company—that they do not have anyone in the network who is qualified to offer an opinion on your case. So, although the consultation may not be scary-expensive, it is a key step in getting your treatment paid for.

This will be your first experience at getting the insurer (or their gatekeeper) to do something that they do not want to do. It's showtime.

How to Debate a Doctor

- Listen to his objections

  Then, go home and write them all down. It will be your job to counter each objection with evidence and facts.

- Take note of his concerns

  Remember that his over-riding concern could well be cost containment. He has to be at least halfway convinced that what you suggest will cost less than what he suggests.

  The doctor's second most important concern may be

avoiding extra work or trouble. You need to demonstrate to him that you will fight all of the battles with the insurer yourself . . . all you need is a referral.

- Bring the right studies

  Come with copies of scholarly scientific studies that prove your point. It is important that these articles be "peer-reviewed." Doctors appreciate peer-reviewed studies.

- Always appease, never confront

  Confrontational attitudes will doom you to failure. You may be frustrated with and furious at this in-network doctor. After all, he is trying to prevent you from receiving your lifesaving treatment. You do not take kindly to this. However, you have to put on a respectful face. You must deliver your facts in the most submissive, sweet, ingenuous sort of way. Disarm him with wide-eyed innocence: "Gee, Dr. So-and-So, do you think?

The Play-by-Play: How I Debated Dr. Two Good Years

- Dr. TGY: "There is a guy named Dr. Sugarbaker. However, if you go to him, you will be disabled."

  Me: "Gee, Dr. TGY, you said that I would be disabled if I went to Dr. Sugarbaker. What did you mean by that?"

  Dr. TGY hemmed and hawed, and looked up and down and sideways. He answered, "Well . . . it's major surgery. You would have six weeks of recovery if you did it." Disabled? I think not. One question, and he overcame his own objection.

- **Dr. TGY:** "There was a study at Sloan-Kettering, and everybody died."

  Me: I couldn't find the study online. So, I called Sloan-Kettering, obtained a copy of the study, and read it. He was right; everybody did die. However, they did not use chemotherapy agents with the surgery, and the surgery was not nearly as extensive as what Dr. Sugarbaker does. So . . . no comparison.

  Two days before our appointment, I sent Dr. TGY a fax, telling him how much I was looking forward to discussing the Sloan-Kettering study with him.

  We went through the study together, and, finally, he grudgingly agreed with me. Objection overcome.

- **Dr. TGY:** "Let's wait three months and see how fast it grows."

  Me: Of course, in my scheme of things, it was a ridiculous objection. Who, with any other cancer, would be happy to sit around for three months just to see how fast it grows? Sort of like fiddling while Rome burns, if you ask me. However, I had to answer the objection, so I pulled out the operative report, "Gee, Dr. TGY, doesn't the fact that there were implants in the omentum, indicate a certain aggressiveness to my disease? He just shrugged, so I moved on to my next volley.

"Dr. TGY," I said, "I had a nice long talk with the local surgeon that you referred me to. Among other things, he said, 'I wouldn't wait if I were you.' That's from the doctor to whom you sent me." Objection overcome.

- Dr. TGY: "There is a local surgeon (contracted with the insurer) who is doing something like Sugarbaker."

Me: The local surgeon had to be dismissed, discredited, demolished. I didn't have to make anything up; I simply quoted what the surgeon said to me, "I've done about twelve of these," he said. "And how many open perfusions (putting the chemotherapy directly into the open belly and distributing it manually, by far the most effective technique) have you done?" "I don't do the open perfusion; I do the closed perfusion (inserting a tube into the belly, pumping in the chemo, and hoping that it gets to all the right places). I've done about twenty closed perfusions, but some of those were for colon cancer." I asked him how his appendix cancer patients were doing. He said, don't know, because I don't follow them." From now on, I will refer to him as "Dr. No Outcomes." Dr. TGY exclaimed, "Hey, I've done more closed perfusions than that!" Objection halfway overcome, but I need to drive the point home.

"If you were getting a heart transplant, would you rather see a cardiac surgeon who had done twelve of them, or a heart surgeon specialist who had done hundreds of them?" I offered. He said, "I don't think Sugarbaker has done hundreds of these."

I opened my folder and handed him a study from *Annals*

of Surgical Oncology entitled "Results of treatment of 385 patients with peritoneal surface spread of appendiceal malignancy" by Dr. Paul Sugarbaker. He didn't say a word, he didn't shrug or roll his eyes he started reading. After a couple of minutes and a couple of remarks such as, "Hmmm . . . that seems like a good chemotherapy regimen," he put down the study and said, "I'm going to refer you to Dr. Sugarbaker! Of course, they are just going to say 'no'."

It worked. I could hardly believe it.

Note the objections, counter the objections, provide the proof, do it without confrontation . . . works like a charm.

Ask for the Referral: A Script

Recently I was asked to help someone ask their Primary Care Physician (gatekeeper) for an out-of-network referral. I knew that I could talk till I was blue in the face, and my advisee wouldn't remember enough of what I said to win the referral. He was new to this game, so I wrote him a script. Perhaps it will give you more ideas of how to ask for your own referral.

The health insurer is not a humanitarian agency . . . it is a business. The most important reason for them to keep you in the network is cost containment. Follow the money.

How, then, do you persuade the health insurer to refer you? By using certain words that are powerful within their own bureaucracy. The only power that you have is these words. What lies behind these words is your power to sue the health insurer. If we did not have the power to sue, they would not spend an extra penny on us.

Here is a sample of how to ask for a referral, using your magic, door-opening words. I have highlighted the words so that, no matter how you speak your peace, you can be sure to use them:

"Dr. So-and-So, I am requesting a referral for my wife Mary to Dr. Expert, who is not in your network. When we met with Dr. Smith, he suggested a colon cancer protocol with systemic chemotherapy. He stated that this is the **standard of care** for Mary's **rare** cancer. Not only is systemic chemotherapy not the standard of care for appendix cancer, but it is strictly **palliative** in nature. People with this **fatal disease** have been **injured** by following it, with their **chances of a good outcome severely decreased**.

Dr. Smith referred us to Dr. No Outcomes, a local surgeon who is contracted with the insurance company. We have done the research. (Present Dr. No Outcomes' resumé here.) Dr. No Outcomes is a general cancer surgeon who has done a few surgeries on appendix cancer patients with **extremely poor outcomes**. He does not do the intraperitoneal chemotherapy with open perfusion, which is by far the most effective technique. As a matter of fact, his last appendix cancer patient spent seven months in the hospital with a perforated bowel, a hole burned in the bladder, and **numerous other complications** costing over a million dollars. Surely you can understand that we would not choose this option, for the good of both your bottom line and Mary's life.

Dr. Expert is the world's expert in appendix cancer. He has done over nine hundred surgeries for appendix cancer, published the papers, done the studies. He teaches other surgeons all over the world how to perform this exacting, complicated and intricate surgery. Most of the long-term survivors with good quality of life and little ongoing medical involvement were patients of Dr. Expert. With certain types of this cancer, he is achieving fifteen-year survival rates of 70% without recurrence. His treatment, per Blue Cross of California, is now the **standard of care** for appendix cancer. (Present the Medical Policy Statement from Blue Cross of California here.)

Dr. Smith told us that he is biased against Dr. Expert because he "skews his results." We are not researchers, nor are we statisticians. We have seen no proof that Dr. Expert does this. As a matter of fact, you can see by this study (Hand them a copy of the study which you have found.) that he includes ALL patients in his statistics, grouped according to certain criteria.

I truly believe that nobody in the Anytown area is **qualified** to provide **curative** treatment for Mary's disease. We think that it would be best, even the most cost-effective, solution to refer Mary to the most qualified expert in the United States for this disease, who can offer her the best chance of a long, quality life.

Of course, I am simply requesting a referral for a second opinion. We think that, if we consult the most experienced expert on this disease, we can be confident that we are following the absolute best course for her continued health and survival.

My helpee studied it. It worked for him. He got the referral. If someone had given me such verbiage when I was stuck between the health insurer and a hard place, I would have read it to Dr. Two Good Years verbatim, looking up and staring at him meaningfully after each sentence. Or, if I couldn't get in to see him personally, I would have turned it into a letter, and faxed it to him.

You can learn the language of the health insurer and out-smart them at their own game, securing the out-of-network referral for the second opinion and proceeding to the consultation with your chosen expert.

CHAPTER 10

Secret Weapon

Win Your Appeal

Armed with my referral and my borrowed frequent flyer miles, I traveled across the country to Washington, D.C. to consult with Dr. Sugarbaker.

I carried with me a huge envelope containing my latest CT scans from the HMO, with the accompanying report declaring that there had been "no regrowth of tumor" after the first surgery.

Only someone who has been Seriously Afflicted can know what it is like to sit in a drafty examining room in a hospital johnny, waiting to meet the individual who will tell you what organs he will leave in and what organs he will take out.

After forty-five minutes, the door burst open and in strode Dr. Sugarbaker, dressed in surgical scrubs and a white doctor coat, coat-tails flying. He greeted me with a warm handshake, "Sorry I'm so late. People come here from all over the world, and it takes awhile to answer all their questions." A surgeon that spends too much time answering questions . . . this is a good thing, I thought.

He had in hand all of my records, tests, CT scans; and he had obviously studied them. He spoke for a few minutes about the disease, then we proceeded to the physical exam.

Now, mind you, I had already undergone a prodigious abdominal surgery during which I was cut from stem to stern. He took a quick look at the abdomen and said, "I see you have a small incision." Small? A small incision? Man, oh man, what is he going to do to me, I thought.

He then moved on to the rectal exam, saying, "This is a really important part." Within a two-minute rectal exam, he was able to feel five small tumors. Holy Moses . . . didn't the HMO tell me that there was no regrowth of tumor?

He left the room, I dressed, and we met across the hall. Now he would finally tell me what to leave in and what to take out. First, he did something that none—repeat, none—of the local doctors had ever done. He hung the films up on a light box and went over them with me, pointing and showing and teaching, "See this white streak here? That is tumor."

There was tumor everywhere. I listened as intently as you would listen to St. Peter at the pearly gates. At the same time, I was thinking, "Wow, am I impressed with this man; he knows every nuance of this disease. Finally, a doctor who knows whereof he speaks. This is horrifying; the local surgeon told me that he had 'gotten it all' and that there was 'no regrowth of tumor'." But I also knew in that moment that I had all the ammo I would ever need to win my appeal with the insurer. They mis-diagnosed me and mis-read the scans. That was all I would ever need.

I returned to Anytown and proceeded to do my research for the appeal. I had no money, I had no lawyer. The appeal had to be a smart-bomb, it had to be air-tight, it had to be unimpeachable. It had to work.

* * *

I have included the full appeal (except for some of my personal attachments) for you to use. I encourage you to study it, to use my language, to plagiarize to your heart's content. But first, so that you can create your own War Documents, I will tell you what research and logic went into it.

- Title page

  All requests to your insurer should be "expedited." Expedited means fast, and that is what you want.

- Table of Contents

  Your appeal is a serious legal document, and you want it to look like one. After you get all of your sections and your attachments together, number them all and write your table of contents. You want to make things as clear and easy and organized as possible for your readers. Furthermore, you want the doctors and bean counters at the insurance company to suspect that you are a lawyer, or that you know a lawyer. So . . . make it look professional.

- Cover letter

  First, formally request the appeal.

  Second, mention the consult and the denial.

  Third, introduce your expert.

Borrow my language. Always emphasize the fact that your appeal is "expedited," and your treatment is "lifesaving." When telling about your medical treatment in the network, include all dates and doctor's names. You want these people to know that you have your facts NAILED DOWN; this will be very scary to them.

- Bullet list of your facts

  Show them your stuff. List out the ammo that you are going to hit them with. No feeling words, just the FACTS. Seeing your legal case here, pared down, in all its glory, will grab their attention and prepare them to read your document VERY closely.

- There is no physician at the HMO with working knowledge of, nor expertise in, my rare cancer—a story of mishaps, mis-diagnoses and near disasters."

  "This is the section where you tell your medical story. No sob story here, just the facts. Your purpose here is to shock them, as in, "Oh man, we blew it! This is a total bombshell! If we don't pay, she may sue the livin' pants off of us or take her story to the media!"

  You have read and studied your medical record. You have taken notes whenever you talked to a doctor or nurse by phone, or visited a doctor in person. So, you have precise information about who made what ridiculous or untrue statement to you and when they said it.

- "Dr. No Outcomes the local surgeon to whom the HMO

refers appendix cancer patients has scant experience, no credentials, and very poor outcomes with this rare cancer, by his own admission."

This is the section where you demolish the local doctor to whom they tried to send you. In some cases, all you have to do is report exactly what he said to you. Then add the phrase "by his own admission." It makes you sound like a lawyer.

First, report your conversation with Dr. No Outcomes. Second, if you can find one, tell of a terrible outcome with this doctor. Third, suggest that perhaps this terrible outcome might be very, very expensive. And, finally, attach Dr. No Outcomes' bio, to demonstrate that he has no qualifications to treat your disease/condition.

- "Dr. Sugarbaker is the world-renowned expert in appendix cancer, with vast experience, impeccable qualifications, and proven good outcomes with this rare cancer."

Prove that your expert has no peer.

State his experience and accomplishments, attach his resumé, and attach the most impressive article or study by him that you can find.

- "Dr. Sugarbaker offers a comprehensive, curative treatment plan based on a detailed physical exam and expert interpretation of the CT scans."

The treatment plan, which you should receive from your expert doctor after your consultation with him, is considered by the insurer to be the most important part of your appeal. They will try to pick this apart and find reasons why not to pay for it.

Of course, you told your expert doctor going in that you are fighting your insurance company. So, he has turned the report of your consultation into a powerful weapon, using words like "tantamount to malpractice."

- "HMO radiologists and physicians misread CT scan of 6/24, missing five areas of cancer nodules found by Dr. Sugarbaker."

Eeeek . . . bombshell, bombshell! If you can prove by the medical record and by the statements of your medical expert that the in-network doctors mis-diagnosed you, mis-read your medical tests, gave you treatment or advice that could cause you serious harm, you have scored a major victory. Make yourself sound like such a 'hot potato, such a botched case, that they can hardly wait to get rid of you and send you on down the road to Dr. Expert.

In this section about the misreading of the CT scan, I juxtapose the statements of the in-network doctors with the statements of my expert, just to make the in-network doctors sound totally unqualified to treat my cancer.

- "Kaiser Permanente, the affiliate with whom the HMO shares 'best clinical practices' (from HMO website), routinely pays for the treatment both with Dr. Sugarbaker and with his associate, Dr. Esquivel."

Your health insurer may have paid before for the treatment which they call "experimental/investigational/not medically necessary"—many times. Shocking, isn't it? Of course, the insurer doesn't want you to know this. From their point of view, the worst thing that can happen is for patients to find each other and to start comparing notes.

This is why, in reality, the insurer does not want you to sue them. It is not because they might lose the lawsuit . . . they won't. They have plenty of money and plenty of lawyers to defend against any lawsuit. The reason why they do not want you to sue is because, once you sue, your case becomes PUBLIC RECORD. Then, trouble-makers like me (or like malpractice lawyers) can look up your case, study it, and learn how to defeat them.

The most likely place to find precedent is on a website or forum for your condition/disease. Ask, "Is there anybody out there with Acme Insurance who has had their treatment paid for? When, what is your name, what is your doctor's name, and how much did they pay?"

Of course, if my HMO had really picked apart this section, they would have realized that I didn't present any specific examples of the HMO paying for Dr. Sugarbaker. As a matter of fact, I didn't present even one example of Kaiser paying for Dr. Sugarbaker—just for Dr. Esquivel. If they had checked into it, they would have discovered that Dr. Esquivel is in-network for Kaiser, and they would have sent me to him.

Hey, a bluff-down is as good as a knock-down.

- "Washington Hospital Center, where Dr. Sugarbaker operates, is contracted with Kaiser and has reciprocity with the HMO."

  If the hospital where your out-of-network expert operates is in-network or contracted with your insurer, you are one step closer to a "yes." All you have to do is call the hospital of choice and ask.

- "The HMO pays as much or more for the local Dr. No Outcomes who knows slim-to-none (by his own admission) and has no results and no track record as they would pay for Dr. Sugarbaker, who is the world's expert on appendix cancer."

  Since it really is all about the money, save your cost containment argument for last. First, get an estimate for your out-of-network treatment.

  Second, find out how much patients have been billed for treatment by Dr. No Outcomes. I accomplished this by pretending to be a potential patient of Dr. No Outcomes. I called his office, "Gee, for some reason the HMO is denying payment for treatment with Dr. No Outcomes . . . could you help me?" "But they pay us all the time," his staff person answered. "Well, I'm doing a little cost/benefit analysis. Could you possibly find out how much the treatments with Dr. No Outcomes have been running?" She consulted with the accounting department and supplied me with actual cases and figures.

All's fair in love and war.

- Conclusion

  You can pretty much quote me on the conclusion. Throughout the appeal, abstain from using any feeling words whatsoever. In the conclusion, you may allow yourself a tiny taste of righteous indignation:

  "All I ask from you is the same fine treatment that you would provide to an HMO member with any other cancer"— inference being that what they are trying to do to you is desperately unfair.

  "It is time to do the right and reasonable thing, adopt a just policy for treating this cancer, and let me go to my lifesaving surgery in peace." In other words, you should be ashamed of yourselves.

- Medical Record

  I know that the insurer already has your medical record. However, you need to attach it, so that it becomes an official part of your appeal.

Date: 8/16/05

From: Laurie Todd
       ID# 00000

To: Appeal Coordinator

RE: Expedited Appeal Request

**Expedited Appeal Request
Laurie A. Todd
8/16/05**

TABLE OF CONTENTS

*Not all of these listed attachments are included here.

123 Maple Street
Anytown, USA 90000
(123) 123-1234
xxx@yahoo.com

August 16, 2005

HMO
Appeal Department
P.O. Box 123
Anytown, USA 00123

Attn: Appeal Coordinator

RE: Case of Laurie A. Todd / Member ID Number 0000

Dear sir or madam;

On 7/18/05 I received a letter from John So-and-So, M.D. denying coverage for treatment of my rare cancer. With this letter I appeal the denial.

On 7/1/05, my HMO oncologist, Dr. Two-Good-Years, requested a second opinion consult on my behalf with Dr. Paul Sugarbaker. The 7/18 letter from Dr. So-and-So (see Att. 1) approved payment for the consultation with Sugarbaker Oncology Associates, while at the same time denying payment for any services that Dr. Sugarbaker might recommend. I was surprised that the HMO would deny payment for services before seeing the report of those services.

Dr. Sugarbaker is Director of Surgical Oncology at the Washington Cancer Institute of the Washington Hospital Center in Washington, D.C. I consulted with him there on 8/8/05. In this letter I offer you the report of this consultation which you have approved.

Per Dr. So-and-So's letter of 7/18, your reason for denial is that "In general, second opinions and other non-emergent services are not covered outside the HMO service area." I appeal the denial on the grounds that—per Dr. Two-Good-Years—I represent the exception to your "general" rule. There is no physician in the HMO network or in the HMO service area who is qualified to offer curative treatment for this progressive and fatal abdominal cancer.

I request an expedited appeal, as my lifesaving surgery is scheduled for October 1, 2005.

In the attached document, I will prove the following facts:

- There is no physician at the HMO with a working knowledge of nor expertise in my rare cancer—a story of mishaps, mis-diagnoses and near disasters.

- Dr. No Outcomes—the local cancer surgeon to whom the HMO refers appendix cancer patients—has scant experience, no credentials, and very poor outcomes with this rare cancer, by his own admission.

- Dr. Sugarbaker is the world-renowned expert in appendix cancer, with vast experience, impeccable credentials, and proven good outcomes with this rare cancer. Dr. Two-Good-Years recognized this.

- Dr. Sugarbaker offers a comprehensive, curative treatment plan based on a detailed physical exam and expert interpretation of the CT scans.

- HMO radiologists and treating physicians misread CT scan of 6/24, missing five areas of cancer nodules found by Dr. Sugarbaker.

- Kaiser Permanente, the affiliate with whom the HMO shares "best clinical practices" (from HMO's website), routinely pays for the treatment both by Dr. Sugarbaker and by his associate Dr. Esquivel.

- Washington Hospital Center, where Dr. Sugarbaker operates, is contracted with Kaiser and has reciprocity with the HMO.

- The HMO pays as much—or more—for the local Dr. No Outcomes who knows slim- to-none (by his own admission) and has no results and no track record as they would pay for Dr. Sugarbaker who is the world's expert on appendix cancer.

. . . .

I. There is no physician at the HMO with working knowledge of nor expertise in my rare cancer—a story of mishaps, mis-diagnoses and near disasters.

I am a 55-year-old white woman who was self-employed as a massage therapist. In November of 2004, I came to HMO South for a check-up with Dr. Primary Care. She performed a complete physical exam and blood tests and pronounced me to be in perfect health.

Four months later, on 3/18/05, I presented myself at HMO South with a swollen belly. I was seen by Dr. Partner. She ordered a CT scan, and I visited her on 3/19 to review the CT findings. In her notes on the visit, she states, "In this encounter I informed the patient that there is a high probability of an ovarian malignancy." (quoted from my Medical Record, Addendum #1, page 30) **(Diagnosis #1)**.

On 3/24/05 I underwent an operation performed by Dr. John Jones of Pacific Oncology Specialists—a standard operation for late-stage ovarian cancer. The pathology slides were submitted to both Anytown Hospital and Johns Hopkins for analysis, and they concurred on a diagnosis of pseudomyxoma peritonei **(Diagnosis #2)**, a type of appendix cancer.

Two weeks post-surgery, I received a call from Dr. Smith, the attending HMO OB/GYN. He said, "You don't have cancer. It is benign." **(Diagnosis #3)**. I then handed the phone to my sister, who is a registered nurse, and Dr. Smith repeated the diagnosis to her.

On 5/9/05, I saw Dr. Jones for the post-operative check-up. He said, "So, you're working with the oncologists at HMO, right?" "No," I answered, "Dr. Smith told me that I don't have cancer." "You have cancer," he continued, "We're just arguing semantics here." **(Diagnosis #4)**. He went on to offer me a 30% chance of recurrence in five years **(Prognosis #1)**. In his notes from this visit, Dr. Jones says, "I suggested that she may want to seek other opinions." (quoted from my Medical Record, Addendum #1, page 76)

On 5/31/05 I saw Dr. Two-Good-Years, my HMO oncologist, for the first time. "What do you think of the 30% in five years?" I asked. "You have two good years left," he said **(Prognosis #2)** "Based on what?" I asked.

"In my fifteen years at the HMO, I have seen two cases of your disease. It took two years before they needed surgery again."

It occurred to me that two patients was a rather small population from which to draw such a conclusion.

II. Dr. No Outcomes—the local surgeon to whom the HMO refers appendix cancer patients—has scant experience, no credentials, and very poor outcomes with this rare cancer, by this own admission.

When Dr. Two-Good-Years realized that I was not interested in serial debulking (repeated palliative surgeries where I would lose more and more colon, finally lose my stomach, then die of bowel obstruction and starvation), he said, "There is a guy at the University . . . I think that he is doing something like Sugarbaker." I offered to find him myself, check him out, and report back to Dr. TGY. I spoke with Dr. No Outcomes at length by phone on 6/30/05, and this is what he said, "I operate on breast cancer, colon cancer, mesothelioma. I have done fifteen closed perfusions (A closed perfusion is not considered curative in this disease.), but some of those were for colon cancer. I don't know how the patients with pseudomyxoma are doing, because I haven't followed them."

Recently, I came into contact with a man whose mother, Jean Jerome, is a member of the HMO with appendix cancer. She was offered the option of surgery with Dr. No Outcomes just as I was. She underwent her surgery at the University on August 8. Some quotes from her son's messages to me: ". . . they accidentally put a small hole in her bladder . . . the surgeon said that he really doesn't have a prognosis . . . how swollen she is . . . she can't open her eyes to see us."

I am not privy to the medical records as you are, but I would suggest that you might want to check and see both how this patient is faring and how much these complications have cost the HMO.

I have attached a copy of Dr. No Outcome's credentials from the UX website. He has no special training nor attainments in the area of gastrointestinal cancers (see Att. 2).

. . . .

III. Dr. Sugarbaker is the world-renowned expert in appendix cancer, with vast experience, impeccable qualifications, and proven good outcomes with this rare cancer.

Dr. Sugarbaker has performed over 900 surgeries for appendix cancer and intraperitoneal chemotherapy treatments. His curriculum vitae appears on the website www.findcancerexperts.com:

"Dr. Paul Sugarbaker is an internationally recognized oncologic surgeon with expertise in gastrointestinal cancers, liver tumors, mesothelioma and soft tissue sarcomas. Currently, he is Director of Surgical Oncology at the Washington Cancer Institute of The Washington Hospital Center, Washington, D.C. From 1986–89 he was Director of Surgical Oncology at Emory University School of Medicine in Atlanta, Georgia. From 1976 to 1986 Dr. Sugarbaker was at the National Cancer Institute, Bethesda, Maryland, where he was a senior investigator in the Surgery Branch as well as Head of the Colorectal Cancer Section.

After graduating from Cornell University Medical College, he spent nine years in surgical training, that included internship, residency, fellowship and basic surgical research at the Massachusetts General and Peter Bent Brigham Hospitals in Boston. He earned an M.A. degree in Immunology from Harvard University in 1983. Dr. Sugarbaker is a member of numerous academic societies that include the American College of Surgeons, Association for Academic Surgery, American Association of Cancer Research and the International Society of Regional Cancer Therapy, of which he is a founding member. He has appointments on numerous editorial boards that include *Journal of Hepato Pancreatico Biliary Surgery, European Journal of Surgical Oncology* and the *International Journal of Surgical Sciences*. Dr. Sugarbaker has authored over 500 scientific articles and chapters. He has developed numerous video presentations demonstrating various surgical techniques. As a recipient of numerous distinguished awards, he has delivered the "Burchenal Lecture" at Memorial Sloan-Kettering Cancer Center and received the E. T. Krementz Award for Best Research Development in Ulm, Germany. In 1999, Dr. Sugarbaker was awarded a Doctor Honoris Causa from the University of Liege, Belgium" (see Att. 3).

Dr. Sugarbaker wrote the book on appendix cancer. You will find a copy of *Atlas of Appendix Cancer and Pseudomyxoma* on his website—

(www.surgicaloncology.com). I have attached one of his 500 published articles to illustrate the extraordinary results that he has been able to achieve with appendix cancer (see Att. 4). . . .

IV. Dr. Sugarbaker offers a comprehensive, curative treatment plan based on a detailed physical exam and expert interpretation of the CT scans.

As you can see from the attached encounter summary, Dr. Sugarbaker has found five areas of tumor on the 6/24 CT scans which were not detected by the radiologists, by Dr. Two-Good-Years or by Dr. Smith at the HMO. Dr. Sugarbaker sets forth a detailed game plan to deal with the tumor present including surgery to remove existing tumor strands and nodules and intraperitoneal heated chemotherapy.

I quote from Dr. Sugarbaker regarding probable outcomes, "The probablity of success at 20 years with this approach [peritonectomy plus intraperitoneal heated chemotherapy] in our experience is 80%. I think that the probability of long-term success with alternative treatments such as serial debulking is 0% at 20 years. I would hasten to add that this [peritonectomy plus intraperitoneal heated chemotherapy] is the standard approach to adenomucinosis from an appendiceal malignancy. The practice of serial debulking is in my opinion now borderline malpractice."

Dr. Paul Sugarbaker's Treatment Plan is attached (see Att. 5). . . .

V. HMO radiologists and physicians misread CT scan of 6/24, missing five areas of cancer nodules found by Dr. Sugarbaker

On 6/28/05, I received a letter from HMO physician Dr. Joe Smith reporting the results of the 6/24 CT scan (see Att. 6). I will compare Dr. Smith's statements with those of Dr. Sugarbaker. (I quote from the aforementioned encounter summary of 8/8/05.):
****

Dr. Smith (HMO): The results show **no masses** or evidence of tumor returning.

Dr. Sugarbaker: There is a small volume of tumor beneath the hemidaphragm, in and around the right hemidiaphragm, and in and around the falciform ligament. There are some strands of tumor in the residual greater omentum.

****

The fifth area of cancer nodules not noticed by the HMO—within the cul-de-sac, was found by Dr. Sugarbaker during the rectal exam.

****

Dr. Smith (HMO): There is a small amount of free fluid which is often found in normal, healthy women.

Dr. Sugarbaker: There is a small volume of ascites within the pelvis.

****

Dr. Smith (HMO): The results show no masses or evidence of **tumor returning.**

Dr. Sugarbaker: She has a small volume persistent and progressive disease by both CT examination and physical examination.

****

Finally, I quote from Dr. Jones' remarks from our post-op visit of 5/9 (Medical Record, Addendum #1, page 76): "I informed her that in my own personal general approach to this problem is a primary resection and **if it is complete,** as in her case, observation only."

We know with 100% certainty now that **the removal of the tumor was not complete.**

Att. 6: Dr. Smith's letter of 6/28 . . . .

VI. Kaiser Permanente, the affiliate with whom the HMO shares "best clinical practices" (from HMO website), routinely pays for the treatment both with Dr. Sugarbaker and with his associate Dr. Esquivel.

- I have attached an e-mail message of 8/3/05 from Patient Smith (see Att. 7). He states that Kaiser paid for his IPHC (intraperitoneal heated chemotherapy) surgery with Dr. Esquivel at the Washington Hospital Center on February 27, 2004. The total that Kaiser paid for the bill—hospitalization plus doctor's fees—was $114,699.92.

  Mr. Smith is pleased to provide a redacted copy of the bill if this is not sufficient.

- I have also attached an e-mail message from Patient Jones dated 8/4/05 (see Att. 8). He states that Kaiser paid for his wife's hospitalization and surgery in December 2001 at Washington Hospital Center. They also paid for a second surgery at Washington Hospital Center in March 2004.

- Dr. Sugarbaker's office informed me that Kaiser has recently paid for the treatment from Dr. Sugarbaker and that they have also paid for it several times in the past. Please feel free to contact Dr.Sugarbaker's office at 202-877-3908 if you need further details about Kaiser's payments to his office.

Kaiser has established a precedent by sending their appendix cancer patients to Washington Hospital Center. By repeatedly reimbursing for this treatment, Kaiser demonstrates that this treatment is their standard of treatment and best clinical practice for this difficult disease.

Attachments 7 & 8: Smith and Jones e-mail messages re- Kaiser payment.
. . . .

VII. Washington Hospital Center, where Dr. Sugarbaker operates, is contracted with Kaiser and has reciprocity with the HMO.

The contract language cited in your denial states: "Members enrolled under the Agreement are entitled to Covered Services only at HMO facilities. . . .

On 8/1/05, I spoke with Ms. X at Kaiser Permanente in Washington, D.C. She informed me that Washington Hospital Center, where Dr. Sugarbaker operates, is contracted with Kaiser. "I am a member of the HMO," I asked, "What does that mean to me?" She replied that, as Kaiser has reciprocity with the HMO, I would be treated as a Kaiser patient. "We honor your HMO insurance."

It doesn't get much closer to an HMO facility than that.
. . . .

VIII. The HMO pays as much—or more—for the local Dr. No Outcomes who knows slim-to-none (by his own admission) and has no results and no track record than they would pay for Dr. Sugarbaker who is the world's expert on pseudomyxoma.

- The estimate for total costs including doctor's fees and hospitalization for my treatment at Washington Hospital Center (per Dr. Sugarbaker's office/Ilse) is $80,000 to $120,000. We have established that Kaiser paid $114,699.92 for the treatment in 2004. These figures include hospitalization and doctor's fees.

- I was able to persuade Marsha at Dr. No Outcome's office to research exactly how much the HMO had paid for a comparable surgery for appendix cancer. We spoke by phone on August 2, 2005. She remarked, "They send people here all the time." Then she checked with the Accounting department for exact figures. She told me that the HMO had funded treatment for pseudomyxoma recently to the amount of $26,000 in doctor's fees and $138,000 in hospital charges, for a total of $164,000.

If you need to know more about how much the HMO is paying to send patients to the relatively inexperienced Dr. No Outcomes, you might want to check on how high the bill is running for Jean Jerome, who is currently in the ICU at UX Hospital with complications.

Dr. Sugarbaker is charging an extraordinarily reasonable fee given his lofty stature in the medical community and his vast experience and expertise with this difficult cancer. The typical surgery and treatment for appendix cancer seems to run in the $120,000 to $150,000 range regardless of the geographical location or the qualifications of the surgeon.

We have not factored in the issue of complications. Complications cost money. Surely, in a disease where even detection of it requires great expertise and eradication of it requires exquisite surgical skill, it makes fiscal sense to send the patient to the most experienced surgeon with the proven track record.

CONCLUSION:

I have a rare cancer growing throughout the abdomen. It is a progressive, fatal disease.

All I ask from you is the same fine treatment that you would provide to an HMO member with any other cancer. You would not say to a person afflicted with breast cancer, "Let's wait around, see how fast it grows, and cut it out again and again as it gets big."

You would not say to a sufferer of colon cancer, "We are sending you to a surgeon who has done less than fifteen colon cancer surgeries, even though there is a surgeon in Washington, D.C. who has done nine hundred colon cancer surgeries. If we send you to the local surgeon, it will greatly reduce your chance of long-term survival. It won't cost us any more to send you to the expert; it will probably wind up costing us less. But we will not send you just because his office is not in Anytown." You wouldn't do it.

I have already been through enough agony with the yo-yo diagnoses, ever-changing prognoses, and the terror of knowing that the HMO missed extensive tumor which was apparent on my CT scan of 6/24. I propose that, now that we have a clear picture of my current disease and what needs to be done to achieve the best result, we go forward with the well-documented treatment that is clearly the standard of care for my rare and difficult cancer.

I request that you fund my treatment with Dr. Sugarbaker and reading of future CT scans by radiologists expert in detecting pseudomyxoma cancer. It needs to be paid as an "in-network exception"; i.e., Dr. Sugarbaker needs to be reimbursed at the in-network rate with no patient responsibility.

When I return to Anytown after my October 4 surgery with Dr. Sugarbaker, you will have the opportunity to assess how a patient with appendix cancer fares when they receive the finest care. More cases of this disease are appearing every day; I suspect that this disease is not nearly as rare as we have believed in the past. It is time to do the right and reasonable thing, adopt a just policy for treating this cancer, and let me go to my lifesaving surgery in peace.

Sincerely,

Laurie A. Todd

Expedited Appeal Request
Laurie A.Todd
8/16/05

Addendum

Complete HMO Medical Report

11/14/04—5/11/05

Find out the name of the Appeals Coordinator, and address it to him/her personally.

Fasten the entire package with an alligator clip, place it in a pristine large white envelope, and mail it certified mail—that will make it look official.

I mailed this War Document on 8/16/05. On 8/19/05, the HMO phoned to tell me that they had approved my out-of-network treatment.

CHAPTER 11

Gettysburg Address:

Win Your Appeal Hearing

A cancer patient, Bill Hernandez recently came to me with a new insurance challenge—the "second appeal," conducted as a hearing. Bill (fresh out of the hospital, after massive surgery and chemotherapy) would be required to appear in person before a panel including both a member of the insurance company bureaucracy and several insurance plan members. He would be allowed fifteen minutes to plead his case.

The insurance company, a PPO, had already paid their allowed amount for Bill's hospitalization. However, they were refusing to pay the expert surgeon at the in-network rate. Which would mean that the surgeon would be paid peanuts for this heroic surgery. Let me get this straight. Surgery is the only curative treatment for this cancer. We will gladly pay everything about your treatment EXCEPT the surgeon? Excuse me . . . what good would all of this hospitalization be if the surgeon didn't show up?

Bill would be bringing exactly the same proof to this hearing that he had used in the initial appeal. He came to

117

me with proof, and a story. We needed to craft a speech that would blow them away.

How does the in-person hearing differ from the written appeal? It is a completely different animal; and, if you don't recognize this, you could write the wrong speech and lose the day.

It differs in four ways . . . if you understand these three differences, you will be able to turn your proof into your very own Gettysburg Address.

Time

In your written appeal, you have all the time (pages) you need to flesh out your case. Fifteen pages, twenty pages. You will not throw anything in your appeal which does not serve to prove your case. However, your goal is to overwhelm the insurer with as much proof as you can muster.

In your in-person speech, on the other hand, you have only a few precious minutes to change those insurance company "hearts and minds." You must sift through all of your powerful evidence and distill it down to the most shocking, outrageous few.

Your written appeal is like a novel; your in-person speech is like a poem. In your poem, each word must be a polished pearl of power.

Audience

All writing is, in a sense, propaganda. In other words, all writing is an effort to influence or to persuade. If we are to have any chance of persuading, we must consider our audience above all.

When you prepared your written appeal, your audience was the insurance company. Of course, these people are caring human beings, trying to do the right thing. However, for purposes of persuasion, you needed to see them as cold-hearted functionaries, interested only in protecting those insurance company dollars and denying you treatment. Your written appeal, aimed as it is at a faceless, massive, monolithic corporate entity, has to be an unassailable legal document. It must address the bureaucracy in its own terms, and it must utilize to the fullest the only power that you have—the power to sue the insurance company. You need to bury your emotions and stand firm.

When you write your in-person appeal, your audience is a small group of living, breathing human beings. Only one or two of these people are employed by the health insurer. If you approach this audience with the attitude of "I will sue the livin' pants off of you if you don't pay for my care," you will offend them, not convert them.

Your purpose with the in-person speech is not to intimidate, but to move them. To make them walk a mile in your shoes, to make them see how absurd it all is. In short, to feel your pain.

Intention

How do you go about putting your audience in your shoes?

First, you must teach. Tell them your story. Teach them about your cancer, walk them through your experience step by step. Don't TELL them how you felt about it. It's like an Impressionist painting . . . simply lay out the events as they happened, and let THEM fill in the feelings.

Once you have given your audience all the facts they need, draw them to the proper conclusion by asking a rhetorical question: "How do we go about removing all visible tumor?" "Sound incredibly complicated?" "Does this seem right to you?"

Insert hook, play out your line, then reel, reel, reel them in.

Delivery

For the written appeal, all that we need to know about delivery is to put our document on quality paper, eliminate all typos, and send it by certified mail. For the spoken appeal, we need to know much more.

We are talking about the short—very short—course in public speaking.

Assemble your proof, write your speech, then practice, practice, practice. Say your speech out loud to whomever will listen. Say it until you practically know it by heart. Of course, you will also have to time your speech, because you only have a precious few minutes to hit your home run and win the World Series.

If I were the star at an in-person hearing, this is how I would proceed.

I would dress in the clothes that made me feel most comfortable and most confident. Before I left home, I would spend a half-hour in meditation or prayer—whatever would clear my head. I would meditate on opening my heart, and also opening the hearts of my audience. No walking in with a chip on my shoulder . . . if a person is hit with anger, their natural response is to reject you, and to lob that anger right back over the net.

I would walk into the hearing room with my head held high . . . looking at each person, reflecting on how we are all just people, here today in the same boat.

My speech would be written down in large type which I could easily follow. I would have copies of my carefully selected proof (doctor's curriculum vitae, a peer-reviewed study or two) for each attendee.

I would begin by thanking them for taking the time today to consider my case, then I would take a deep breath and begin.

How to deliver a written speech of this nature? By reading a sentence or two, then looking up and gazing meaningfully at your audience. Look at them as though you were trying to burn the meaning into their very souls. Keep engaging them, continuously look up and hold their gaze.

Your intention is to make them feel something, to cause a reaction. After the third paragraph, you should start to see some reaction. Eyes open a little wider, mouths may even drop open. Be sure to capitalize or bold your most powerful sentences, so that you can deliver them a little more slowly, with a little extra power and concentration.

End your speech with your simple request, and leave the room with your shoulders squared, trailing clouds of dignity.

The Speech

My name is William Hernandez.

I am forty years old.

I have a rare cancer—pseudomyxoma peritonei—otherwise known as appendix cancer.

Appendix cancer does not look like other cancers . . . it does not act like other cancers. There is no diagnostic test for appendix cancer—even CT scans, which are our best tool, are unreliable at best. In the hands of radiologists who are not trained in visualizing appendix cancer, they are useless.

Appendix cancer does not act like other cancers. It—unlike colon cancer— is not aggressive enough to be susceptible to systemic chemotherapy . . . unless all visible tumor has already been removed. We call this "complete cytoreduction." Then, when only microscopic tumor cells are left, they can be treated effectively by applying powerful heated chemotherapy directly to them, introducing the chemo agents directly into the open abdomen, massaging them into the organs.

How do we remove all visible appendix cancer tumor, when that tumor doesn't look like any other tumor, it is spread all over the abdomen, it is adhered and stuck on all sorts of critical organs, it is hiding in all sorts of nooks and crannies, coating ligaments, multiplying in scar tissue from previous surgeries?

Just to give you an idea what is involved in cytoreduction surgery, I quote from the TrueHealth Medical Policy statement dated 12/1/2005.

This TrueHealth document states that cytoreduction and heated chemo- therapy are now officially deemed "medically necessary" for my rare cancer. They go on to describe the surgery:

"Cytoreduction initially involves mobilization of the liver, exploration of the diaphragm, mobilization of the stomach and lesser sac, exploration of the bilateral abdominal gutters, pelvic recesses, and mobilization of the large and small bowel with examination for tumor deposits along their entire length. Surgical resection can be extensive, depending on the extent of disease, but may include partial gastrectomy, splenectomy, and resection of the tail of the pancreas, omentectomy, multiple small bowel resections, ileocecal resection, rectosigmoid resection, uterine resection, and multiple peritonectomy procedures. The surgical procedure is followed intraop- eratively by the infusion of hyperthermic chemotherapy, most commonly mitomycin C. Inflow and outflow catheters are placed in the abdominal cav- ity, along with temperature probes to monitor the temperature. The skin is then temporarily closed during the chemotherapy perfusion, which typically runs for one to two hours."

Sound incredibly complicated? It is. After I tell briefly the story of my treatment within the TrueHealth PPO network, you will know that there is no doctor in this network even remotely qualified to offer an opinion about my rare appendix cancer, much less treat it.

On August 15, 2005, I visited my Dr. Johnson, my Primary Care Physician, complaining of pain on my right side under my rib cage. Dr. Johnson scheduled an ultrasound, which revealed a large stone in the gall bladder. On August 31, successful surgery to remove the gall bladder was performed (wrong diagnosis #1, wrong surgery #1).

On September 9, 2005, I visited Dr. Mills of XYZ Hospital for what I assumed was a routine post-op visit. During that visit, Dr. Mills informed me that he had biopsied some tissue during my surgery, and that it came back positive for "signet ring cell carcinoma." A CT was performed, and it was determined that I had gall bladder cancer (wrong diagnosis #2).

On September 20, I proceeded on to Dr. James Andrews, Chief of Surgical Oncology at University of Anystate Hospital. He confirmed the diagnosis of gall bladder cancer and told me that—given this diagnosis—I had one or two years to live, and that I should go home and get my affairs in order. I went home and did as instructed (wrong diagnosis #2 confirmed).

Since I am a diligent patient, and my life was on the line, I sought a second opinion at Highly Regarded Cancer Center in Anycity on October 21. Drs. Oncologist #1 and Oncologist #2 had the tissue samples re-tested at their lab, which then issued the following statement: "We feel that this is NOT gall bladder cancer . . . it originated from the appendix" (finally, a correct diagnosis).

Drs. Oncologist #1 and #2 then told me their proposed treatment plan for appendix cancer. They stated that they would treat it with systemic chemotherapy—the "colon cancer regimen." They immediately started me on systemic Avastin, Oxaliplatin, 5-FU and Lecovorin, with great suffering to me including peripheral neuropathy. After six months, my toes and fingers were completely numb (palliative treatment, rarely effective, horrific side effects, no cure).

They went on to state firmly and unequivocally, "THERE IS NO SURGICAL OPTION FOR THIS DISEASE" (untrue, totally wrong advice, totally eliminates the only curative treatment for my disease).

What effect did all of this wrong chemotherapy have on my appendix cancer? None.

During the one-year period that I was on the most aggressive systemic chemotherapy available, I underwent CT scans every two months. Although, according to Dr. Oncologist #2, the second scan showed "marked improvement," I ended up at the end of one year in worse shape than I started, with "liver involvement, colon involvement, diaphragm involvement, omental caking, and pelvic ascites (malignant fluid in the abdomen).

It was at this point that I met Mr. John Smith. Mr. Smith not only had the same appendix cancer that I did, but he was a MEMBER OF INDEPENDENCE BLUE CROSS. Mr. Smith explained to me that what we have is called pseudomyxoma (PMP), and that surgery by an expert surgeon who has done hundreds of surgeries FOR APPENDIX CANCER/PMP was our only chance at a good outcome or a long life.

Mr. Smith had undergone the cytoreductive surgery endorsed as "medically necessary" by TrueHealth PPO Network. His expert surgeon was Dr. Expert in Othercity, and even though Dr. Expert was out of the network— Independence Blue Cross had paid for the entire treatment AT THE IN-NETWORK RATE. I was flabbergasted.

I immediately visited Dr. Oncologist #1 and asked if all this was true. "Do I have PMP, and is there a surgery available for it?" I asked. He said, "Yes." Then he went on to say, "We do not do that surgery here at Very Highly Regarded Cancer Center, it is very risky, and you will have to go to the most experienced surgeon who has done the greatest number of these surgeries for PMP. There are few experts who do this type of surgery, etc., etc."

DR. ONCOLOGIST #1, THE IN-NETWORK DOCTOR TO WHOM I WAS REFERRED, KNEW ALL ALONG THAT THERE WAS AN EFFECTIVE SURGICAL OPTION FOR ME. INDEPENDENCE BLUE CROSS PUT ME THROUGH AND FUNDED A YEAR'S INAPPROPRIATE CHEMOTHERAPY TREATMENT WHICH HAD NO EFFECT ON MY CANCER, HARMED MY HEALTH, AND DELAYED MY HAVING THE ONLY TREATMENT THAT COULD HELP ME.

Through my own extensive research, I found the three top surgeons in the world for this rare type of cancer. Dr. Expert in Othercity was eminently qualified (see attached credentials), so I decided on him for my treatment. Besides, I assumed that all would go smoothly with TrueHealth PPO Network, as they had already paid for Mr. Smith's surgery for the same cancer with the same surgeon.

One week before my scheduled surgery, I was informed by Dr. Expert's office that my insurer had decided not to pay for my treatment, the objection being that it was "experimental." Within a week's time, while preparing for massive abdominal surgery, I wrote an extensive appeal; TrueHealth PPO reversed their decision and decided to pay for my treatment with Dr. Expert. They offered to pay the entire hospitalization at the in-network rate. The only piece of the treatment for which they denied was the surgeon's fee.

On August 8, 2005, I underwent the surgery and intraperitoneal chemotherapy with Dr. Expert. The surgery was a complete success. He was able to remove all visible tumor, and he performed all of the complex procedures explained above. He has given me an 80% chance at no recurrence of my PMP/appendix cancer.

This treatment is ALL ABOUT THE SURGERY. Without Dr. Expert, there is no treatment. Dr. Expert's fee was $18,000. TrueHealth PPO Network is planning to pay him $1,200. DOES THIS SEEM RIGHT TO YOU?

All that I expect is the same level of treatment that you would provide for any other patient suffering from cancer. Would you tell a person with breast cancer, "We know that what you really need is surgery. However, we don't have the skills to do it here. So . . . why don't you go ahead and do chemotherapy, even though it won't do you any good." DOES THIS SEEM RIGHT TO YOU?

I request that you reimburse my expert surgeon at the in-network rate and let me go about my long, quality life in peace.

Mr. William Hernandez

Att. Qualifications of Dr. Expert

As you can see, a lot of ammo can be made to fit into a fifteen-minute speech.

A week after Mr. Hernandez delivered this Gettysburg Address, he received a call from TrueHealth PPO Network, notifying him that they would be reimbursing his expert surgeon at the in-network rate.

CHAPTER 12

Resistance:

Make Them Pay It All

The health insurer had rolled over and conceded defeat. I had in hand the official letter stating that they would pay for all of the out-of-network treatment with my expert doctor for a ninety-day period. My surgery date was on the books. So . . . I let down my guard and assumed that the war was over. I could spend the next three weeks eating bon-bons and watching court TV, right?

Wrong.

At this point, Ilse said, "Now, on to the next battle." What battle? "You need to get the insurer to sign a SINGLE-CASE CONTRACT *stating that they will pay a certain percentage of our actual billed charges, not delete any charges, and not bundle any codes. If you cannot get the agreement before your surgery, you will have to come with a $20,000 deposit for Dr. Sugarbaker's fee." Man, oh man. I am supposed to persuade an insurance company to sign a paper stating that they will pay a specified percentage of an amount that they don't know how much it is yet? In two weeks time? I doubted my ability to pull this one off.*

* * *

Even though the insurer has agreed to pay, they still have a few tricks up their sleeve. If you don't hold their feet to the fire before your treatment and make them agree not to use their tactics to reduce payment to the hospital and to your chosen expert doctor, you could be inundated with bills AFTER your treatment. Thousands of dollars worth of bills. Hundreds of thousands in bills.

A serious cancer treatment with complications can easily run in excess of $300,000. I would have gone broke if I had been responsible for paying even ten percent of the bill for my out-of-network treatment. If you let them, the health insurer will use tactics of deletion/bundling of codes, paying at the out-of-network rate, denying payment for all sorts of line items—all in order to contain costs.

If your doctor/treatment of choice is out of the network, and not contracted with your insurer—and he gets stuck with a drastically reduced payment by your insurer—he may be able to bill you for the balance. If, however, your doctor of choice is contracted with the insurer, he is obliged to accept whatever payment your insurer deems "usual and customary."

If you are a member of an HMO, they will automatically deny payment to any doctor out of their network. In other words, you have no "out-of-network benefit." You fight this objection by proving that no doctor IN the network is qualified to treat your disease/condition.

If you are a member of a PPO or POS, you may have an "out-of-network benefit." In this case, the insurer may approve your treatment, but they will pay it at a lower percentage. This will result in drastically reduced payments by the insurance company to the various providers (hospital, radiology, pathology, doctors, etc.). Furthermore, this so-called benefit could require YOU to pay anywhere from 20% to 40% of your medical bills. You will go just as broke paying 20% of the bill for a serious hospital stay as you would paying 100% of it.

You fight this objection exactly the same way, by proving that they have to pay the in-network rate because none of the doctors in the network is qualified to treat your disease/condition. Or that the only curative treatment for your disease is not offered within the network.

Either way, it is to your advantage to persuade your insurer—if your doctor of choice has no managed care contract with them—to hammer out the terms of payment with your expert doctor and sign the single-case contract . . . BEFORE THE SURGERY TAKES PLACE. Then, there are no surprises for you AFTER your surgery.

Now for the short course on persuasive letter-writing: You must accomplish three tasks in order to achieve a successful letter. First, you must write a powerful letter—a letter with a little pathos, a lot of intimidation, and a call to action. Second, you must get your letter to the right person, one who has the power to make a decision right now. And, third, you must carbon copy the right people who will check up on your addressee. Copy the Insurance Commissioner in your state, copy the Medical Director of the HMO. If any of your in-network doctors are helping you, copy them, too. Copy your expert doctor's office, particularly if he is very well-known and your insurer may have heard of him.

This letter has to hit its target with no detours. So, if your insurer stonewalls you when you ask to whom it should be sent, it's time to call your friends at the state Office of the Insurance Commissioner. Explain the urgency of the situation and ask to whom this letter should be addressed.

Notice how I praise my addressee, saying that the Insurance Commissioner's Office spoke very highly of her. Very sneaky way to put her on notice that I have spoken to the Insurance Commissioner . . . to someone she KNOWS at the Insurance Commissioner's office.

The letter follows. The trick is to bully them and tug at their heartstrings at the same time.

The $20,000 Letter

Ms. Anne York/Appeals Department
HMO
P.O. Box 123
Anytown, USA

Dear Ms. York;

The HMO approved my lifesaving surgery and chemotherapy with Dr. Sugarbaker in Washington, D.C.; for that I am most grateful. I will leave Anytown on 9/29 and undergo the surgery on 10/4.

I have now been presented with another insurance mountain to climb. I inquired of the Insurance Commissioner's office as to how to proceed, and they spoke very highly of you, so I am asking you for help. Dr. Sugarbaker's office has asked me for a $20,000 deposit for the surgery, unless the HMO and Dr. Sugarbaker's office can come to an agreement on how much (or what percentage of billed services) the HMO will actually reimburse.

It has been Dr. Sugarbaker's experience over the last twenty-three years that insurers—by bundling codes or deleting charges—often reimburse only a fraction of the surgeon's costs. Ilse, Dr. Sugarbaker's office manager, cited a case where the insurer assigned a new CPT code to an extraordinarily complex fifteen-hour surgery and—instead of paying $15,000 as billed—they reduced the claim to $1,500. The surgeon who is going to save my life needs to be paid for his efforts. The way that this has worked in the past with Kaiser and Dr.

Sugarbaker's office is that they have arranged a conference call between Dr. Sugarbaker's office, a financial person at the HMO who is at managerial level, and the insured. During that call, the HMO and Ilse—the experts on billing and reimbursement—hash out the potential pitfalls line-by-line and come to a fair and reasonable understanding of the reimbursement.

I ask that you put me in contact with the appropriate manager in the financial department of the HMO who could work out the fine points of reimbursement with Ilse and me—so that I do not need to supply a $20,000 deposit to Dr. Sugarbaker. And it needs to happen within the next two weeks . . . before I leave for surgery.

If I do not succeed with this part of my work with the HMO, I will need to ask my sister to loan me her life savings. Rather than make such a request and incur such a debt, I need to bring the HMO and Dr. Sugarbaker's office to the table so that they can come to an understanding and I can go to my lifesaving surgery in peace.

Sincerely,

Laurie Todd

cc: Dr. Sugarbaker

Do you suppose that, by now, the poor HMO thought that I had a lawyer hidden in the woodpile? I certainly hope so.

I had called the Insurance Commissioner's office. "Send it to Anne York," the gal told me, "She has been at the HMO forever and can really get things done." I thanked her profusely and wrote my letter, which worked. Two days later, Anne York called me and gave me the name and number of the person who had the authority to negotiate with my expert doctor's office regarding reimbursement.

I called this financial manager, then called Dr. Sugarbaker's office and hooked the two of them up. They horse-traded together for a day or two, and an agreement was reached.

CHAPTER 13

The Troops:

Muster Your Network of Help

*It was not my idea to ask for help. I was lunching with a
friend, pressing on towards my surgery like a one-man army,
when she asked me, "Would you consider asking for help?"*

*I didn't have to think long . . . I needed help. "Yes," I said.
Then I went home and tried to figure out what asking for
help looked like.*

*I will always remember the first person whom I asked
for help, because it signified a major shift in my approach.
It was the day that I opened my heart. I called Dale, a
former client. Dale had been a social worker/therapist at the
Veterans Administration for over twenty years, helping Viet
Nam veterans with post-traumatic stress disorder. Just the
ticket, as I was headed off soon to war. "Dale," I said, "I need
a session. Well . . . maybe two." He said, without a moment's
hesitation, "You can have all the sessions you want."*

*At first I couldn't imagine sending out an appeal myself.
It felt like advertising your own birthday. It felt like I was
humbling myself. However, it gradually dawned on me that*

the appeal had to come from me. The appeal had to come from me; folks needed to hear my voice. And, perhaps more importantly, I needed to know that being humbled is not a bad thing.

I had one proviso . . . I would not ask for money.

I composed a letter, telling an entertaining, lively and hopefully honest version of the story. Then I listed what I needed: groceries, paper and ink, a haircut, a massage, frequent flyer miles, someone to be a point of contact during the upcoming surgery, further ideas on how to make a go of it during All This.

As I printed the mailing labels and sent out the letters, my feeling about this whole endeavor started to shift. My heart had already been opened by all of this life-and-death stuff, but I felt a further opening. A refining of my feelings, a clarity, a lightness.

Help started pouring in. And compassion started flowing out—from me. It was, I believe, the result of my asking. I felt so "at one" with anyone who was old or lame wheelchair-bound that it became downright embarrassing. I could see them with my heart. It was all I could do not to reach out, wrap my arms around them, scoop them up and bring them home.

One afternoon, as I sat in the cafeteria of the HMO waiting for another doctor appointment, a man emerged from the food line, making his way slowly towards a table, leaning heavily on his walker for support. The tray of the walker was laden with a cup of coffee, a doughnut and two bananas. I couldn't take my eyes off him; I ached with his vulnerability. Just then, he leaned too far to one side, lost his balance, and the walker tipped over, spilling his breakfast on the floor.

It was all I could do not to rush to his side. And I would have, but an able-bodied couple stepped in, righted the walker, retrieved the bananas and fetched him another cup of coffee. I cannot separate myself from suffering anymore. Through asking for help, we not only receive help, but we grow in compassion.

* * *

You have survived and recovered from your first surgery/treatment. You have learned your way around the health insurer and showed them who is boss, securing firm payment for your upcoming treatment by the world's expert in your disease/condition. Now you can finally sit around and drink milkshakes and watch Oprah, yes?

Sorry. You have been out of work, sitting in the hospital or recuperating at home for months. Your business or your job is gone, or soon will be. You can't afford your hairdresser. You are buying day-old bakery items. So much research and correspondence . . . you are out of computer paper and stationary and printer cartridges. To put it bluntly, you are running out of money.

Worst of all, you are feeling isolated. All of those clients or friends or customers or co-workers are going about their lives, while you sit and worry and wait to undergo your next round of medical intervention. Some of your friends probably want to help you, but they don't know how. Others may not even know what happened to you.

It is easy enough to compile a mailing list, write a lively story of your misfortune, list what you need, and send your story to everyone you know. The hard part is opening your life to the world, and admitting that you can't do it alone. The reward for doing this is that you become kinder, softer, more tender. Best of all, you get to know your circle of friends in a new way.

Muster the troops

- If you are not up to it, you might want to appoint someone to sort out the offers, collect donations, contact the network.

- Consider asking for e-mails or responses by mail. You may not want to deplete your limited energy talking to a hundred people and telling the same story over and over.

- After the first appeal, you can collect e-mail addresses, turn them into a group, and start sending out a weekly e-mail newsletter. Putting your experiences and feelings down in writing once a week can be therapeutic. And, since your friends and family will now always be up-to-date on the story, you will not have to tell it repeatedly.

- Make a "Help" file. Put all of the offers for groceries, haircuts, etc. in there. Then, you can pull one out when you need it.

- Forget about sending thank-you notes. NO THANK-YOU NOTES! You are the Seriously Afflicted person for now; this is a new station in life, and the usual rules do not apply. Besides, you have other fish to fry, and no time to observe social niceties. You are busy saving your life.

- In each weekly newsletter, include a Gratitude Report, where you give attaboys to whomever has especially lifted you up that week. I used initials only, so that the helpers could know who they were but not be "outed" publicly. People seem to really enjoy this part of the communication.

People in the network learn how to give help, and how to ask for help themselves. One friend—she treated me to a manicure—said, "Before I got your letter, I expected my husband to know what I wanted. I expected him to read my mind. You showed me that it is OK to ask for what I want." Hey, we teach what we need to learn. My loneliness was eased, and the network got the opportunity to hear what it is truly like to suddenly find oneself in Really Bad Trouble. I nearly slid over the edge of life, then came back and told the tale. I called it "bringing back the goods." The truth about it was my gift to those who helped. We will all near the edge, so it is good to know what lies there.

When you are suffering, ask for help. When you ask for help, people will not only help you, but they will thank you.

Asking for help is a gift that we give the world, and, in so doing, we are also gifted.

CHAPTER 14

Troop Morale:

Train Your Network of Help

Since day one of All This, I found myself at odds with certain family members and friends. As a matter of fact, it felt as though I was spending most of my time explaining to people what it was like to be Seriously Afflicted. I spent six months arguing. With everybody.

I wasn't taking this the way they thought I should. I wasn't acting like a Hallmark-card-type cancer victim. Except for the occasional dark night of the soul, I never stopped joking. I cried plenty . . . don't get me wrong. But I also found much in my situation that was hilarious. This might have seemed inappropriate to some; but, for me, to stop laughing would have been to stop living. Instead, I mined the rich vein of irony and black humor and just plain absurdity inherent in All This. I found that, when fear and suffering started closing in on me, a good laugh opened up a little space, gave me room to breathe.

I never—repeat, never—tore my garments and asked, "Why me?" I may, on the eve of one more medical nightmare, have asked, "How much can one person stand?" But that is a different question.

Although I was in Bad Trouble, this was still my life—not a pile of misfortunes. If anything, it was suddenly richer than my previous humdrum existence. A big adventure, my hero's journey . . . a journey tailor-made for me. To me, cancer is not the enemy, as in "He fought a brave battle against lung cancer." It is not evil, nor is it shameful. It just is.

I've noticed that some who are in Bad Trouble understand it very differently than I. Many treat cancer as an enemy outside themselves. ("He battled cancer.") They say, "I am cured, I can now go back to my life the way it was. It is not my destiny to have this cancer, so I will put it behind me and get on with my life."

I would rather make peace with my cancer. Cancer is not some critter outside of me, like a virus or a bacterium. It is my own cells mutating—part of me, gone wild.

Everything that the body does is to preserve itself and its life. Cancer is no exception. These massive tumors were my body, reacting to the terrible toxic stresses of our modern world, and doing the best it could to save me. I give it its due . . . it was my cancer, conceived and grown in me. I name it, claim it, thank it and move on. And life moves on, which is its way.

I also differ from many in that, although I do fervently desire to put medical intervention behind me, I do not want to forget about my illness, nor do I want to go back the way I was. I was not healthy, my life was not the way it needed to be. I choose to be changed by my cancer, to make cancer my teacher and inquire of it what it wants me to learn.

There will be those who say, "Cancer is bad. You will never make me believe otherwise." To you I say, live by the metaphor that works for you. For me, however, it is a short, slippery slope from cancer being bad to me being bad. To me being bad because I am suffering. Let me speak for those who would rather make peace with the suffering and let it go . . . to enlist their suffering in service to compassion rather than to fight, fight, fight.

Probably the most thorny part of All This, aside from the first gruesome deadly conflicting diagnoses, has been the reaction of some friends to my illness and, hence, to me. I can rationalize and explain and excuse it like crazy; but, at the time, it hurt.

✢ ✢ ✢

I offer the following list for those who would accompany you on your hero's journey. And for you . . . so that you can take these remarks lightly.

The ten things not to say

- "What were your symptoms, when did they happen, in what order did they appear, what made you finally go to the doctor, etc?"

  Slow down and think about why you are asking. After participating in several interrogations about my symptoms, I realized that people were asking for their own benefit, so that they would not fall into the same manhole that I did.

- "You have to have hope."

    Yes, I know . . . people love the word "hope." For me, the
    verb that goes with "hope" is "to cling." Clinging does not
    appeal to me, nor does it feel empowering.

    I hope, I hope that the surgery is successful, that I will be
    in the "good" ten/twenty/whatever percent. For me, hope
    is a futile attempt to make things turn out a certain way
    because I want them to. Magical thinking. I aspire to that
    place beyond hope and fear, where I am not so attached to
    outcomes. For me, this is peace.

    People say to me, "But you have to have hope," "You've got
    to give us hope," or "Surely you couldn't have gone all the
    way across the country to have that surgery if you didn't
    have hope."

    I got so tired of arguing that I looked up the word "hope."
    It means "to long for with expectation of obtainment." If I
    hope for a sunny day, I expect that, because I hope, it will
    turn out that way. If I hope for a cadillac, do I expect one
    to turn up in the driveway? Does the world really work that
    way? When people pray that their cancer be taken away,
    does that make it happen?

    I will apply my usual disclaimer—if hope is what you need,
    by all means have it. Most people never question the word.
    I would like to be the one to finally do it. Hospitals are
    named for it: "City of Hope." But I need to speak for those
    who, when all well-wishers insist on hoping for them, find
    the Hope word strangely creepy. Sad. Discouraging. Passive
    in the extreme.

I did not approach my lifesaving treatment with hope. Having researched the alternatives, I felt that the extravaganza in Washington, D.C. was my best and only shot at a cure. I fervently desire that that treatment will prove successful, and that the cancer will not recur. However, the reason why I fought so hard to get the most expert treatment in the world was NOT because I hoped that it would cure me. It was so that, no matter what happened in the future, I could rest peacefully in the knowledge that I had done my best to preserve one precious life.

So many times I have seen the terrible depression that descends when the hoped-for outcome doesn't come to pass. Perhaps in foregoing hope I try to spare myself this further suffering: But I hoped . . . how could my hoping be in vain? I have seen people ask, "I prayed that my cancer be taken away. How could my prayer not be answered? Is God not listening?"

Ah, expectations. Are they the source of all sorrow?

Suffering is a natural part of life. Fires, floods and nasty accidents are just as integral a part of life as lottery wins, sunny days and miraculous escapes. Everyone will age and experience some diminishment of powers. Most will face some illness or injury in this lifetime. I simply do not see these occurrences as bad or as a punishment, and I feel much happier if I do not hope for things to turn out a certain way. Not attached to outcomes—that's how I aspire to be.

- "You must be so angry, always asking, "Why me?"

No, never.

Stressed out, yes. Afraid, definitely. Grieving, you bet. Confused, often. But never angry that this has happened to me. I am not interested in practicing anger just now. Besides, the fact that I got this disease makes perfect sense to me. My whole generation was a chemical experiment; not everyone's genes can stand up to the lifetime barrage of enviro-toxins to which we have been subjected. The whole question of "why me" implies that someone did this to me on purpose, or that I intentionally did this to myself.

Which brings me to the next dumb remark. . . .

- "Where did your life go so drastically wrong?"

It didn't.

This is what I call the "repressed feelings" defense. You caused your own cancer by being neurotic. The implication being that the questioner has no issues herself and will therefore escape cancer. Sorry, but I have news for you. Emotionally healthy people get cancer. Priests and rabbis and psychiatrists and enlightened yogis and miserable people and happy people get cancer. All of these people get cancer—some more than once. Many of them get well and go on to live long, quality lives. Does that mean that their lives were going drastically wrong when the cancer grew, and now their lives are suddenly "right"?

You insult me when you suggest that I am such a psychological basket-case that I caused this cancer myself. A life does not have to go that drastically wrong in order to get cancer.

- **"You will make it because you are strong."**

I do not aspire to be "strong"; I aspire to be tender. I am learning that strength is in tenderness. My strength is in brotherhood with my fellow living creatures. The more I feel, the more I open myself to every deep feeling, the better I can cope. Strength may be important to a steelworker; it is of little use to me.

- **"I was thinking of my daily worries, getting all riled up . . . then I thought about YOU, and I realized that my problems are NOTHING compared to yours."**

Gee, thanks.

Do you have any idea how often I hear this one? Folks think that they are complimenting me by sharing this revelation. Thanks, I chuckle, I am now the train wreck of a life that makes everyone feel else feel better!

Hey, it's natural to look for someone who has it worse than you. There is a word for it—*schadenfreude.* Believe it or not, even people who have cancer do this. If I have just suffered two major surgeries, I take note of the guy who has had six. Believe it or not, many of us these days have more than one cancer—appendix cancer and breast cancer, thyroid cancer and prostate cancer, brain tumors and melanoma. I thank my lucky stars that I am not one of them!

If you tell me how insignificant your troubles are compared

to mine in order to make yourself feel better, it will definitely work. But it won't do much for me. It's OK to think that your troubles are less disastrous than mine; just don't share it with me.

- "I didn't call (write, e-mail) you because I didn't know what to say."

  And now I have to tell you what to say?

  It took you six months to figure out to say to me that you didn't know what to say? All you would have had to do is say it, and we could have gone on with our friendship.

- Crying. Don't do it.

  Do I have to offer a disclaimer? Hey, if you feel better surrounded by weeping well-wishers, far be it from me to discourage you. As for me, I want to let you know that this is no time for crying. I am exceedingly alive. I will probably be waltzing around the earth for years to come. Save your crying for at home; it is no comfort to me. As a matter of fact, all of this crying and boo-hooing and tearing of hair makes me feel like a scene from "Terms of Endearment."

- "I don't know if I could do what you are doing."

  Hey, I didn't raise my hand and volunteer for this.

  Either I get treatment for my cancer, which involves two humongous surgeries and a radical chemotherapy that is fraught with danger, or I don't. I have undergone the treatment. Does that make me brave? No, it makes me a scaredy-cat. If I don't do the treatment, I will have to face the most terrible gradual nasty death from abdominal cancer that you can imagine. I'm in it, and I need to do what I need to do.

Besides, if you live long enough, you WILL have to do some version of what I am doing, whether you think you could do it or not.

- **"If this ever happens to me. . . ."**

Newsflash . . . it will happen to you.

I don't mean to be Cassandra, the Prophetess of Doom. However, aging, illness and diminishment of powers is the way of all living creatures. Remember Ram Dass, guru of consciousness back in the 1960s? I saw a documentary about him recently . . . he was in a wheelchair, paralyzed on one side after his recent stroke. Still writing, still giving talks. Of course, the words come a little slower now, and the topic of his talks has changed. Life moves on . . . that is what life does. I do not have the energy anymore to try and stop the river.

The vast majority of us will not live hearty, independent lives, totally free of medical involvement until we die at the age of ninety-seven by falling out of the porch swing with a margarita in our hand. Just isn't going to happen. Most of us will suffer some type of chronic illness, maybe not as shockingly sudden as mine, but just as serious. We will endure surgeries, terrible drug therapies, hospitalizations. It is good that we remember this, but I do get a little weary of being the one who has to explain it to you.

In addition to the things that you should not say to a cancer patient, there is one thing that you should not do—abandon them. Not because it is not nice, nor because you will hurt your friend. But because suffering is part of life. And if you embrace it—lean into it—you get to have more life. And, if you run away from it, you get to have less. Less tenderness, less understanding, less peace.

One day I was visiting with Jens, the friend who has helped me more than any other with the larger issues of my Medical Troubles. The big picture, the underlying assumptions. I told him that many had found a way to distance themselves from me over the last year. Jens' wife suffered from a rare cancer several years ago; Jens was her advocate and her champion. So, he always knows whereof he speaks, and he always stands ready to help.

"Before Teri died, we were invited to thirty or forty Christmas parties every year. We made a game of it, laying out the invitations and deciding which ones we would attend together, attend separately, make a brief appearance at, and so on. Do you know how many Christmas parties I was invited to after Teri died? Zero. None."

I understand that cancer terrifies you. You do not want to be anywhere near it. You don't want to believe that it will ever touch your life. Certainly, you can run away and put off suffering until a later date. If you show up, though, you and your friend will be in this together. You will learn to open your heart even when you are afraid, and you will become less judgmental of your friend and of yourself. Later on, I promise you, all of these skills will come in very handy.

CHAPTER 15

P. O.W. Camp:

Survive Your Hospital Stay

I have experienced the hospital, big-time—first for a week, then for forty days and forty nights. I wish I could tell you that I lounged around on fluffy pillows, attended at all times by solicitous nurses and attentive doctors. Not so! Brace up, Seriously Afflicted One. You are about to be exiled to the Cancer Gulag.

* * *

The insurance is on board, you are appreciating your network of people, and you have a surgery date. You have packed your slippers and your trashy novels, and you will soon be off to the hospital.

- Get vaccinations

  If you want to find the world's worst drug-resistant infections, look in a hospital. Our grandparents avoided the hospital at all costs, seeing it as a death-house. Mainly because of infections. Those infections of our grandparents' day have had eighty years to morph into the contagion of your nightmares.

Before going anywhere near the hospital, I ordered up vaccinations for pneumonia, meningitis and the flu. No doctor told me to do this. My sister the R.N. alerted me to vaccinations, and I learned on the Internet what vaccinations I would need. Remember, you are managing your own case.

Furthermore, keep an eye on those nurses and make sure that they glove up.

• Bring a caregiver

. . . one who can stay with you every day all day. If you are going to be very sick and weak after your surgery/treatment, you should have at least two caregivers, so that someone can be with you 24/7. Why? Because the nights are the worst. There is less nursing coverage at night; the nurses at night are sometimes not the caliber of the day nurses. It is dark, you are sick, you are scared. One person cannot do this duty 24/7. Bring two caregivers.

In the middle of one endless night, I threw up all over myself. The last nurse in had moved the call button so that I couldn't reach it. I was alone. Lying there as the vomit cooled, I thought, surely this is the lowest point of my life.

Your caregiver is your advocate and cheerleader and medical bodyguard. If you have to pay someone to do this, pay them. Beg them. Bribe them . . . whatever it takes. It could mean your life.

I was most fortunate to have my sister, who is a registered nurse, stay with me every step of the way through both hospitalizations. I might possibly have gotten through the week-long stay without her, but the forty-day siege would have killed me.

You think that I exaggerate? One day in while I was in the hospital, a couple of LPN's were giving me a sponge bath. I started hallucinating and having trouble breathing. Nobody noticed. My eagle-eyed sister noticed, and ran for an R.N. "Something is wrong with my sister!" she said, "You need to check her oxygen levels!"

The R.N. came running, there were no oxygen levels. I was experiencing a pulmonary embolism. All havoc broke loose then, and I was saved. People die from these embolisms. It is likely that, without my hero sister, I could easily have slipped away.

Even if your hospital has the best nurses in the world, there just are not enough nurses in this day and age. Bring a caregiver.

- **Protect yourself from well-wishers**

  Disclaimer, disclaimer! I have been told that some people who are in the hospital prefer that their friends and family visit and call . . . circling the wagons, as it were.

  Perhaps one's desire for company depends on how really sick one is. However, I do believe that I speak for a segment of the population out here who can only cope with one caregiver during the worst of times. If this is you, do not tell your vast network of friends and family what room you are in. Or, you may want to tell them expressly not to write nor to send cards nor flowers. If you are as sick as I was, you will be so sick that you don't give a rat's patoot about anything. You will be too weak to open cards. The smell of flowers, like everything else, will make you bilious.

As you check into the hospital room, immediately disconnect the phone and put it in a drawer. You are sick. You have tubes. You couldn't get to the phone if you wanted to. Besides, you are in no mood to shoot the breeze with armies of well-wishers.

- Locate the nearest grocery store

Before you are allowed to leave the Cancer Gulag, you will have to be able to eat, pass gas and poop. You will exist in a parallel universe—one where polite conversation consists of "Did you pass gas?"

Lord knows I tried, but I just could not force myself to choke down the hog swill that passed for food in the hospital. The cartons of milk were warm, the mashed potatoes were cold. Rubber chicken. Warm apple juice. It was loathsome.

I would surely have starved were it not for grocery store food brought in by my sister. I had had most of my innards removed, had my digestive system rebuilt, and had developed pancreatitis, which makes one really, really nauseous. Also, I developed drug-resistant infections, and I was taking powerful antibiotics with a side effect of nausea and vomiting. Water made me vomit. The only foods that I could stomach were strawberries and watermelon.

• Be prepared to fight to stay in the hospital, or to fight to get out of the hospital.

Before I checked in, I believed that, in the modern healthcare system, my biggest problem would be persuading them to keep me in the hospital long enough to get well. Perhaps others have been booted from the hospital prematurely if their insurance coverage runs out. However, in my case, I was fortunate/unfortunate enough to have a medical team who was not beholden to my insurer. So they were prudent . . . oh, were they prudent!

Sis and I had to fight like beasts to get me sprung out of there. They would have kept me in that wretched hospital bed, on IV meds and total parenteral nutrition, until my body and spirit gave up. There seemed to be no plan to let me out in the foreseeable future.

One day, about thirty days in, I reached my end. Until that moment, I had been too sick to cry. However, finally, I cried, "You've got to get me out of here. My spirit is broken."

They said, "You have to have these IV meds for your drug-resistant infection." My sister said, "You need to find oral versions of these drugs so that she can go home." They said, "You can't go home because you are vomiting inter-mittently." I protested, "There is nothing wrong with my stomach. I am vomiting because you are giving me anti-biotics that have a side effect of nausea and vomiting. You give me the drugs, and I throw up, just like clockwork." Sis added her voice to the chorus, "Just give us anti-nausea drugs to take along with the antibiotics, and she will be fine." "She is not eating enough to go home." "She can't stand the food. She eats everything that I prepare for her." It was a world-class dust 'em up fight.

Of course, in retrospect, I realize that my prudent expert medical team was simply trying to ensure that I was out of danger before I left the hospital to fly all the way across the country. After forty days in the hospital, though, I knew in my bones that there was nothing but more misery for me in that hospital—more suffering, more infections, more deterioration.

If your friend or loved one has had a serious illness or injury and spent a good long time in the hospital, know that she has not been relaxing in a peaceful haven, getting a backrub, enjoying herself at the spa. She has been on the firing line, in the trenches. Your friend returns as a soldier returns from the war zone—post-traumatic stress and all; she needs your patience and your understanding.

CHAPTER 16

Veterans' Benefits:

Make Social Security Pay

I saw an advertisement on television the other day for a lawyer—he was offering to help you to get on Social Security Disability. "What you deserve . . . get out what you paid in . . . we can help you." Where, you might ask, do these disability lawyers get the money to buy television commercials? People are trying to get on disability because they cannot work and have no money!

My sister the R.N. told me stories of patients of hers who died while waiting for their Disability ship to come in. This seemed exceedingly unjust and unfair to me—Really Bad. So, I rolled up my sleeves, put on my avenger hat, and prepared to make Social Security do my bidding.

* * *

Apply for Social Security Disability

It works like this. Social Security Disability takes its own sweet time making a determination on your case—at least seven months. People with terminal diseases or terrible injuries

often die waiting for their cases to be decided. So, even though
S. S. Disability doesn't start paying until five months after the
date on which you were disabled (What are we supposed
to live on for five months?), you generally receive at least
several thousand dollars of "back pay" when you are finally
approved. If you hire a lawyer, he takes half of this. Why not
do it yourself?

The government and its money are not soon parted. Since it
will be at least seven months before any benefits start flowing,
it would be best to apply as soon as possible. If you are too
sick and tired or otherwise goofed up to apply, have someone
help you. If you wait too long, you will either be dead or well
(and not needing the help) by the time they get to you.

There is a powerful urban myth floating around about S. S.
Disability. We hear—and come to believe—that it is so difficult
to apply for it that no normal person could possibly figure it
out on their own. If you are capable of doing your own taxes
. . . heck, if you can fill out a job application . . . you should
be able to apply for disability. I did it, I am receiving S. S.
Disability, and I am not dead.

Some persistence is required. Over a several-month period,
I filled out not one, but two fifteen-page forms which included
medical information, lists of what activities, movements, etc.
that I could perform on a daily basis, addresses and contact
information for my doctors. None of this is rocket science, if
you have kept records since the beginning of your injury or
illness.

Have you ever watched the court shows on TV? I'm not
sure where they find the type of people who give cell phones
to their boyfriends, get into bogus business deals, and bail

their ne'er-do-well relatives out of jail. Have you ever noticed how many of them are on disability? What is the matter with these folks? They hurt their back, have Attention Deficit Disorder, are afflicted with carpal tunnel syndrome. CARPAL TUNNEL SYNDROME? You have a life-threatening disease. You have been through terrible surgeries and chemotherapy. If these deadbeats can get on disability, so can you.

The first thing to know about S. S. Disability is that it is not "asset driven." In other words, you don't have to lose all of your assets and be poor as dirt in order to get it. Other programs, such as state aid of various types and Medicaid, require that you have $2,000 or less to your name, no car, no family jewels and be camping out on someone's couch in order to qualify. Not so S. S. Disability. All you have to do is have no income and not be able to work.

The first application is entitled "Disability Report/Adult." The first thing you will need to do is read the instructions. If anything is left out or answered improperly, the whole process will be delayed another month or more. Somewhere along the line, someone in the know advised me: The more info, the better. So I decided to inundate them with more information, attachments, etc. than they could possibly ever want.

Section 1 is simply contact information.

Section 2 is "Your Illnesses, Injuries or Conditions and How They Affect You." Before you go any further, gather up your medical records, your appointment calendar, your resumé and whatever else you will need to reconstruct your medical and work history. This should be just a matter of pulling files, as you have all aspects of your illness filed away in one drawer.

First, you describe your illness. My illness is relatively rare, so I attached a paper from the *Annals of Surgical Oncology* describing the disease and telling how dire and life-threatening it is. When you state the name of your illness/injury, be sure to mention that it is serious, complicated, debilitating, life-threatening, incurable, terminal—or any combination of the above which may apply. Don't assume that they know how serious your illness is. Don't be shy about it. You have to impress them at every turn that your illness/injury is Really Bad.

In your answer to the question "Why did you stop working?" you can pull out all the stops. Here is how I answered the question: "I had extensive surgery for cancer. They removed uterus, ovaries, omentum and a tumor the size of a volleyball. They also had to resect the sigmoid colon and sew it back together. Pseudomyxoma is a fatal disease." I could have said, "I had surgery" and left it at that. But I want to give them as much detail as possible, and I never want to miss an opportunity to stress how serious my condition is.

Section 3 is "Information About Your Work." Dig out your old resumes, tax returns—whatever you need to reconstruct the last fifteen years of your employment.

Remember, this is not a job interview. You're goal is not to impress anybody with what lofty positions you have held. It's more like an IRS audit. Don't tell them any more than they need to know. If I had gone back more than fifteen years, I might have found some easy, sedentary jobs that I could, perhaps, eventually do again. Instead, I stuck to my fifteen years and listed my careers as a massage therapist (fourteen years) and a realtor (one year). After two major abdominal operations plus chemotherapy, there would not be a snowball's chance of my either pounding the pavements selling houses or standing up doing massage all day long.

In Section E of the Work Information, they list activities such as walking, standing, reaching, etc. that you did while engaged in your work. You need to reflect on your work, and make it sound just as strenuous as it was. Do not underestimate the amount of standing, kneeling or reaching that you did. In other words, it was so strenuous that there is no way you will be doing it again any time soon.

Section 4 is Information About Your Medical Records. You will work from your medical record and your appointment calendar, if you use one. When they ask you "What treatment was received?", give detail and be specific, always leaning on what gruesome procedures or tests were performed on you and how serious they were. I arranged the doctor visits in a strategic order, listing the specialist surgeon who would be doing my upcoming surgery last. I put him last for most impact, because he would be performing a thirteen-hour surgery plus chemotherapy—a treatment comparable in seriousness and risk to a bone-marrow transplant.

Section 6 asks you to list every medical test that you have ever undergone. Impossibly difficult, if you have a serious illness. During my first hospitalization, I probably had three dozen blood tests. I called S. S. Disability, and they told me that it would be acceptable simply to indicate which tests had been done, tell where they were done, and, in the column titled "When done" just say, "See medical record."

Congratulations. You have completed the first step towards receiving S. S. Disability. Make a complete copy of the application for your new "S. S. Disability" file. Now, attach a copy of your medical record and put the application in the mail per instructions. Call them a week later to ensure that they have received it. In my case, they managed to lose it, so I had to copy my copy and re-submit.

Two months after submitting this first paperwork, I traveled to Washington, D.C. and underwent the treatment with Dr. Sugarbaker. In all, I spent nearly two months in D.C. When I returned home and was able to climb the stairs to my condo, I pulled out the file and called S. S. Disability, "Hi folks, I had a massive surgery. How are things going with my claim?" "Yes, we know about your surgery; I just talked to your doctor in D.C. Now we will mail out another fifteen-page application, so that you can tell us how you're condition has changed since you applied." Man, oh man. Sure am glad it wasn't brain surgery.

The second application is the "Function Report/Adult." I wanted to be sure that they remembered just exactly what type of an ordeal I had been through, so I began with a cover letter. Notice that I review the whole sad story, never missing a chance to tell how serious it all is:

Your cover letter

Dear Ms. So-and-so;

In March of this year, I was stricken with a rare appendix cancer called pseudomyxoma. On March 19, I underwent a five-hour abdominal surgery where the surgeon removed my uterus, ovaries, appendix, part of my colon and a volleyball-sized tumor. I spent a week in hospital at HMO South. After that first operation, I filed my application to Disability Determination Services.

The HMO had no experience in nor knowledge of my rare cancer. So, during the summer, I found the world's expert on pseudomyxoma—Dr. Sugarbaker in Washington, D.C.—and persuaded the HMO to pay for the treatment.

In August I traveled to Washington, D.C. and consulted with Dr. Sugarbaker. When I spoke to you by phone two weeks ago, you had contacted Dr. Sugarbaker's office and been informed of my latest medical treatment. On October 4 of this year, I underwent my second huge abdominal surgery in a seven-month period. This second surgery lasted ten hours.

Dr. Sugarbaker removed my gall bladder, spleen and much of my remaining colon. He also removed many tumors, scraping them off of the underside of the diaphragm, the pancreas and the entire lower abdomen. He also stripped out the peritoneum, which lines the entire abdominal cavity. Then he filled the abdomen with heated chemotherapy drugs and closed me up. The chemotherapy treatment continued during the next four days.

Then the complications started. Sepsis (a hospital-based blood infection), a drug-resistant urinary tract infection, infection of one of the surgical drains, pancreatitis, a psychotic break which left me in restraints. And the most dangerous complication—a pulmonary embolism. I remained in the hospital for forty days . . . I could not have imagined that a person could be so sick.

After I left the hospital in D.C. on November 5, I stayed with friends there for three weeks—until I could muster up enough strength to fly back across the country. Even after three weeks, I still could not walk more than one-half block. I couldn't lift the gallon of milk in order to pour myself a glass.

I did not know how I was going to be able to manage crowded airports and a six-hour flight. About that time, my friend Mary Smith called, "I've decided that I would like to fly to Washington, D.C. and bring you home." Which she did, and for which I am very grateful.

Now I am home. When we talked by phone, you asked me to submit another form detailing my ability to perform daily activities since this latest round of medical intervention. I have enclosed the "Function Report," and I look forward eagerly to a determination and some possible help for me.

Best regards,

Laurie Todd

Would you refuse help to this person? Include a cover letter. Tell a compelling story. As I wrote my letter, I thought, "You should be ashamed of yourselves, granting benefits to these folks suffering from stress over their divorce while people die waiting for help." I decided that I would state my case in such a way that the only thing they could say would be "Where do we send the checks?"

Living on Social Security Disability

I completed all the paperwork. I made the follow-up phone calls. Then, one day, $5,000 mysteriously appeared in my checking account. A call to the bank confirmed that, yes, I was now on S. S. Disability. The entire process had taken ten months. Benefits do not begin until five months have passed, so I received five months of back benefits.

When I informed friends and family that the S. S. Disability had finally come through, the usual response was, "Great." Great, yes. And also problematic. I had been without income for nearly a year, so the small infusion of money was certainly welcome. And, as with the health insurer, I felt exceedingly righteous in my victory. However, bottom line, you can't live on Social Security.

Sorry, baby boomers. Unless you are living with your elderly parents or sleeping on someone's couch, you can't live on Social Security. The amount of your benefit depends on how long you have worked, how much you have paid in, etc. I was fifty-five years old and had worked since I was eighteen. My current benefit is $1,030 per month. My mortgage plus condo dues is $1,100 a month (pretty low for this day and age). You do the math . . . already the numbers aren't adding up.

My monthly health insurance premium is $265 a month. We haven't even started with the phone bill, the heat and electricity, prescription medications or food. Folks seem surprised that I cannot scare up some type of state aid to make up the difference. Believe me, I tried. In order to receive state assistance of any type, my assets need to be down to $2,000—and no hiding of assets, or I am in big trouble. If I spent down my already slim assets to $2,000, I would be behind on the mortgage within a month. I did manage to obtain food stamps for three months between the operations. Guess how much food stamps gives you for all that trouble? One hundred dollars of food a month. You can't live on it. And, as soon as you get on Social Security Disability, all state aid is cut off.

You may ask, how do people live on Social Security? Because they do. If they own a house, they can spend their assets down and rent out part of the house in order to make ends meet. Or, if they have skills to offer—accounting, carpentry, massage therapy—and are able to do a little of it, they can earn some money on the side. They can? You thought being disabled meant "I am a living vegetable and can't do anything at all." Not exactly.

On S. S. Disability, you are allowed to work either a little or a lot. This year, if you are disabled and you work for someone as an employee, you are allowed to earn $860 per month. Not a princely sum, but you might be able to keep going if they offer you some health insurance along with your part-time job. If you are self-employed and disabled, you are allowed to earn $690. Yes, it's less. Don't ask me why. Another attempt to discourage people from being self-sufficient? One more way to beat the impoverished, but still ambitious person with a big stick?

Unless, of course, you are doing a Trial of Work. It takes an entire government publication to explain the Trial of Work, but here is my simplified version: You are feeling somewhat better, and you want to see if you can work again. But you are not sure if the body/mind will stand up to it. It will take some months of working before you will be able to decide. So, Social Security allows you a nine-month Trial of Work.

During those nine months, you can earn as much as you want and still collect your benefits. If, after those nine months, you want to continue earning your big money, Social Security will cut you off. If, on the other hand, you need to retire to your sick-bed again and stop earning more than $860 or $690 per month, Social Security will continue to pay your benefits.

Those of us with cancer have a special situation. We may become disabled and "able" again several times in our lifetimes. We get better, live for years, then have a recurrence, a surgery, whatever and are disabled once more. Do we have to wait six to ten months every time we need to call on S. S. Disability again? Fortunately, no. If we have been disabled once, we bypass the waiting period. The wheels of the government turn at a glacial pace, however; and I have no idea how soon, in real time, the benefits would be restored.

What about Medicare? Can't you receive Medicare because you are disabled? Sorry, baby boomers. You don't receive Medicare until you have been on S. S. Disability for two years. Somehow, you have to keep paying for your health insurance until then.

Don't you at least get some re-training, schooling, vocational rehab? Not until your case has been reviewed once. That means that I have nearly a year to wait until I could qualify for vocational rehab or job placement services. Hello! People! I had abdominal surgery, not brain surgery! Am I supposed to sit around on my duff reading true-crime books for a year, leaving home only to visit the food bank?

This whole Social Security Disability system is so odd and non-sensical . . . will I eventually get vocational rehab if I am better after a year (Now you can re-train.), or if I am not better? (Now you can re-train, because you are not well enough to perform your previous work.) I have no idea.

You do not need a lawyer to apply for Social Security Disability, and you do not need to be without assets to get it. You just need to fill out the applications properly and in a timely manner, and state—in every way possible and at every opportunity—that you are unable to work.

CHAPTER 17

Healing:

Find Your Gardening Chi

After my first surgery, I was weak. After the second surgery seven months later, followed by forty days in the hospital, I was disasterized. I threw up at least once a day, visited the loo twenty times a day, and couldn't stand any food but melons and macaroni and cheese. I was vague, zombie-like. I wondered how much better I would ever get.

But the worst part, the strangest part of post-surgery was the total lack of . . . ambition. Initiative. Energy. I did not care about anything, I didn't want to do anything. I lived night and day in the same pair of pajamas; I couldn't muster up the energy to change them. It was all I could do to shuffle from the bed to a chair in front of the television, where I sat for hours watching the home decorating channel.

Also, I was exquisitely sensitive to sounds, light, temperature. I couldn't stand loud noise, particularly loud voices. Harsh light hurt. And I was cold, I was hot. I couldn't sign my name, open my own pill bottles or cut my own nails.

Further, I could only stand so much conversation or human interaction. My attention span was about two minutes. I found listening a chore, a long story or an involved joke unbearable. I would stand up in the middle of a conversation, with no excuses or farewells or how-do-you-do's, go into my room and close the door. Phone calls were even more taxing; three minutes, max, and I was done. I would say, "My telephone arm is tired."

I pondered the question: What is it that I am lacking? What does massive medical intervention take out of a person, energy-wise? What got all used up, what was stripped away? The only word that I could come up with was "chi." Of course, I had encountered the word before. It meant something like "life energy." Well, over the next days, weeks and months, I became a connoisseur of chi. I got my PhD in chi. I discovered many types of chi, and I rejoiced as they re-appeared—one by one, by some deep logic.

* * *

Computer Chi

When the desire to use the computer first surfaced in me, I sat there helplessly—I had forgotten how to type. Now, mind you, I have typed—as graduate student, secretary, typesetter, word processor, writer—for over thirty years. How strange, I thought. I would have been alarmed, but I didn't have the energy. I typed two-fingered for awhile. It took a few more weeks before Typing Chi kicked in. It rushed back all at once, in an instant.

Rising Up Chi

There is a special energy that allows us to get up. To climb stairs and to lift ourselves out of the bathtub. This chi seems to reside in the quadriceps muscles, which after the surgeries were weak out of all proportion to the rest of my body's weakness.

When Sis and I arrived at our friends' home after my hospital ordeal, I did not have the strength to open the car door. When my sister opened it for me, I had to grasp the door frame and haul myself up and out of the car. No rising up chi.

Even with a raised toilet seat (sure sign of geezer-hood), it was a herculean effort sitting down and rising up. A bath was out of the question, because I would have had to get all the way down and, more impossibly, all the way back up. We settled on supervised showers.

Finally, my sister had to return home to Boston. After all, a husband, several pets and Thanksgiving celebrations with her in-laws awaited. So, loyal friends took over my care, fussing over me and changing my dressing and coaxing me to eat. They also encouraged me to start climbing stairs; they must have intuited the vital significance of rising up chi to my recovery.

At first, I could only—with much effort—climb three steps up and three steps back down. I could only accomplish this feat by leading with the stronger quads of the right leg. Each day, I was able to add a step. Then, one day, all at once like the typing chi, stair-climbing chi returned in one fell swoop. It was as though a great sealed reservoir of climbing energy had been pried open and poured into me.

Waking and Sleeping Chi

Surgery wreaks havoc with waking and sleeping chi. I went through an extended period of listless limbo, neither alert nor relaxed. A sort of troubled zombie state from which I had no relief. I say "zombie," because it refers to the walking dead. Neither alert nor relaxed, I was restless, terribly restless. My take on it is that the deep body systems—the autonomic nervous system, the primal sense that we have of being alive, the lizard brain—do not know what to do with themselves after these terrible medical interventions. We are not dead? How could this be?

Really, the organism is not made, wired up nor constructed to survive such rearrangements of its inner workings, such injury, such trauma. I picture dials spinning out of control, scrambling desperately to find some sort of balance. Where are our organs? What has happened to us? How will we now survive?

Not only are the sleeping/waking dials totally out of whack; but, all the other regulatory systems are in a total uproar as well. I was hot, I was freezing. I was hungry, but could only eat three bites. I was sociable, I suddenly needed to be alone. Determined for a minute, then defeated for a week. None of these feelings was emotional per se—they arose from the belly and washed over me like a tsunami. Spinning, spinning out of control—with me along for the ride.

In the hospital, I didn't want to sleep . . . couldn't bear it. I would turn the light on and off, on and off a thousand times a night. It wouldn't take Sigmund Freud to figure out why; sleep is a little like death. The poor ravaged body just did not want to go there. It was probably three months before I slept with a modicum of peace. Sleep improved, and I began to dream. Alertness gradually returned, and I began to feel alive again.

Standing Up Chi

Before All This, I was not aware of standing up chi. Standing up requires a lot of energy. Standing chi has become the most obvious measure to me of health to me, and it has come back the most gradually. One degree at a time . . . there must be a hundred degrees of improvement still to come. In the hospital, after five minutes of standing, I experienced an urgent need to lie down. Five minutes of standing remained my limit for a month or so. Standing in line at the bank was out of the question. I couldn't stand long enough to brush my teeth.

Even now, five months after the Mother of All Surgeries, I cannot stand still very long. Running a mile is easy, but I do not have stamina for standing. As I wait in line at the grocery, I start to feel a bit queasy and uneasy; I start looking around for a chair or a bench.

Standing chi returns slowly . . . as slowly as water wearing away stone.

The good news about this is that I am prevented from doing a menial job which requires standing: greeter at Wal-Mart, waitress, cashier. Whatever I do to support myself as I return to the Land of the Living, I will have to use my brain rather than my standing chi.

Working Chi

My work, before All This started, was massage. As my mind started to clear and the tiniest bit of ambition began to arise, I consulted my brain to see if I remembered how to do massage. I had been a massage therapist for fourteen years; and, yet, I didn't remember a thing. Not one move. That fourteen years of skill-building could have been wiped out was . . . well, disturbing. It would have been devastating; however I didn't have enough on the ball to worry much about it.

One day, nearly five months after the big surgery, I set up the old massage table and decided to see what I could do. Just like typing chi and rising up chi, it came back suddenly, like magic.

Gardening Chi

There was no garden during the Year of Bad Medical Trouble. In fact, gardening became downright odious to me. I, who loved to plant seeds, would not even venture into the garden.

The reason for this aversion didn't dawn on me until gardening chi started to bubble up. I was out on the deck, emptying out the two-years-ago pots, when it came to me. Digging in the dirt was like burying something. Dust to dust.

Once I had made the connection, the spell was broken. As I look out the French doors, I see a dozen pots in all stages of poking two leaves up, showing their unique shapes, and blooming.

As for sex chi, salsa dancing chi, croissant-making chi, and home improvement chi . . . give it a year or two, they will all come back.

CHAPTER 18

Peacetime:

Beyond the Land of the Living

You're not bad because you're suffering

There has, apparently, been a rash of suicides among the survivors of Hurricane Katrina. The poorest of the poor are not killing themselves . . . they are accustomed to living on the narrow ledge of survival, without the illusion of safety or security. No, it is the professionals who are ending their lives.

I picture them as doctors, lawyers, accountants. They have spent long years at university, piling up student loans. After they graduate, they go out into the welcoming world and start their own practices. They rent fine offices, establish professional relationships, invest in equipment—finally, one day, the clients are rolling in, and they can buy a lovely home.

All of this comfort, progress and prosperity is ever so dangerous. It lulls us into thinking that we are safe, that nothing will ever change. However, life always changes. Life moves on, because that is what life does. Are you ill? Life will move on. You are wealthy? Life will move on. You are suffering? Life will move on. Pleased with life as it is? Life will move on.

I am reminded of the things people say when they experience a "near miss." Almost drove off the cliff, nearly drowned, exited the bank as the robber was heading in. They say, "I barely got out of the building on 9/11 . . . my prayers were answered, I know that God was protecting me." Sometimes, if they are the due and diligent type, they continue, "I must have been spared for a reason. I have something more to do with my life."

What about the thousands of other equally worthy and worthwhile souls who perished in the same buildings? Was God not looking out for them? Did they not fervently desire to live? Did they have nothing further to do with their lives?

To me, a burning building or a tsunami or an inoperable tumor is nothing more or less than life—in all of its implacable, unstoppable glory—moving on.

If we are faced with an unstoppable moving force, what then shall we do? We can't contain it or manage it or bend it to our desires.

We all, myself included, sometimes succumb to magical thinking. We, the Seriously Afflicted, search for a diet or a remedy or an emotional healing that will allow us to appease life, which is moving on. To affect it, to seduce it, to force it to give us some more of what we want—health. I call it the "after the fact" diet. Sorry, we have had cancer. The horse is out of the barn.

I would like very much to believe that I could make the cancer not recur by something that I do/don't do. It would give me back some illusion of control. However, the terrible pitfall to this type of magical thinking is that, if I can do something to stop my misfortune, I must have done something to cause it. I am a fool, a failure, a weak animal culled out from the herd. I am bad because I am suffering.

The flip side of believing that God has spared you is believing that God has punished you. The slippery slope to shame is greased with stress, self-loathing, isolation. I am now ashamed because I am suffering.

Which brings us back to where we started—the professionals from New Orleans who committed suicide. Their offices were swept away in the flood. Their patients/clients scattered to the four winds. Perhaps their homes were damaged beyond repair. Insurance wouldn't cover it . . . they were not in good hands with their insurers. All insulation from trouble torn away by one terrible wall of water.

Sometimes life moves on gently, sometimes with a big bang. But it always moves. It moves as our parents age, it moves as our businesses flourish and fail, it moves as our children grow and move away. What then shall we do when life moves, so as not to be crushed by its force? I can think of only one course: Let go. Keep letting go.

After my Year of Living Dangerously, I wanted to scoop those professionals up, turn them upside-down and shake them. You didn't cause this, I would tell them. It is not your fault.

Besides, you are not about this money, these possessions, this stuff. Stuff comes and goes. What is the Bible verse about piling up treasures here on earth, where rust can gobble them up and thieves can break in and steal? There is mercy in such a statement: Let the stuff go. It is going to go anyway. Clinging to it can only cause immeasurable pain. So much pain that the pain might sweep your life away with it. Losing all your stuff is not a tragedy; losing your life because you lost your stuff is.

One day—early on, soon after the first surgery—a casual friend invited me for coffee at a bustling Starbucks. She asked a few perfunctory questions about my recent happenings, then started filling me in on her life, "My business is just getting so busy that I'm going to need to hire an assistant and . . . you know how I volunteer down at the Veteran's Hall? Well, I just met this guy, and he is really nice and . . . my daughter needs a new prom dress and. . . ."

Although I was sitting not two feet from this gal, I felt a million miles away. I was trying ever so hard to listen, but all I could hear was "Blah, blah, blah . . . gurgle, gurgle, gurgle." As though I were listening from underwater.

The crowd, the blah-blah, the smells—I couldn't get out of there fast enough. I knew in that moment that my life had changed forever. Since none of my friends had ever had Big Medical Intervention, I had to devise a metaphor to explain it. It came to me in the form of a fable:

Beyond the Land of the Living

One day, I was la-dee-dahing around in the Land of the Living. Paying the bills, putting oil in the car, meeting for coffee—you know, all of the everyday activities that people do in that land. Then, one day, unbeknownst to me, a giant skyhook maneuvered into position directly above my head, moved silently down and snatched me up. It carried me a great distance, then dropped me down unceremoniously in the Land of the Dead. I was alone there . . . people were horrified by me. And, furthermore, I now spoke a different language.

At first, all I could do was shake my head, dust myself off, and try to figure out where I was, what the rules were, and how to survive here. Then, one day, as I became accustomed to my surroundings, I looked out into the distance and saw that I was, indeed, in a different country. And there was a river separating the Land of the Dead from the Land of the Living. Over time, I made my way to the river. I would have to cross it if I were ever to make it back to the Land of the Living. It was far to the opposite shore. I knew, to my sorrow, how easy it would be to drown.

As I stepped into the water, I nearly lost my footing. I realized that, if I did not unload some baggage, I would surely go under. Possessions, unsuitable friendships, outmoded attitudes—one by one they had to go. I took a few more steps and was nearly washed away. Work had to go, false pride had to go, resentment had to go.

Finally, I hauled myself out of the water and back onto solid ground. I looked around at the Land of the Living, this place that I had struggled so long and hard to reach. And, I no longer belonged. I sat with my former fellows, and all I heard was "blah, blah, blah." Forgive me, I don't speak your language anymore.

So I picked up my ever-so-much lighter burden and set about backpacking my way through the Land of the Living to a new place.

I am a work in progress; I am trying to find out what moving on from a year of Serious Affliction looks like.

For some cancer veterans, their fondest wish is to get back to the way they were before. They want to put this unsettling, unpopular, unfortunate experience behind them and get back on solid ground. I deeply understand this desire.

Indeed, many friends and family are anxious to place me firmly on solid ground. They ask, "When are you going to start doing massage again? You are cancer-free, it's all over. Isn't that great? Aren't you happy?"

Not exactly.

So, in order to explain how it feels to pop out on the other end of Serious Affliction, I had to devise another story:

Isn't it great?

Once upon a time, a man goes to his business. It is his own business, in his own office building. A mighty earthquake strikes, and the office building falls down around his ears. He crawls out of the wreckage and heads for home. He pulls up in front of his house; it, too, has collapsed. All that is left is a pile of burning rubble. In a daze, he steps out onto the curb and into the street and is hit by a bus. He wakes up in the hospital with two broken legs and two broken arms, and the doctor says, "You've survived! It's a miracle! Isn't it great? Aren't you delighted?"

Now, I don't feel such a need to hit people between the eyes with the seriousness of what I have been through. I now say: Going back is the last thing I want to do. I have seen truth. I have fought against injustice and I have won victories. Much has been required of me.

I have balanced on the knife edge between life and death and faced it all with my eyes open. I stand here now a little kinder than I was before, more compassionate and less judgmental. I have grown an infallible gut-o-meter that will not allow me to do anything I don't want to do. I am cut loose from my previous worries, and I speak my mind without hesitation. Although I was often in Bad Trouble last year, it was also the finest time of my life. That solid ground that I clung to was just an illusion; I am much more comfortable surfing the shifting sands of life as it moves on.

Why on earth would I want to go back?

For about five minutes, I thought that moving on meant leaving this illness thing behind. Honestly, I tried. But the gut-o-meter told me that I needed to linger here awhile, helping and being helped, teaching what I want to learn.

I just returned home from a session with Dale, my ever-loyal volunteer psychologist. At the end of our session, he said, "I did have a medical go-round myself . . . nothing like yours, of course. I had several cancerous spots removed from my skin—melanoma." So not rare, so many of us getting so many cancers so young. Such insufficient health insurance, such non-existent government help.

My practical sister keeps asking me when I am going to get a job. I answer, "When I get the book done and in book form." I really think, "When hell freezes over."

What can I say . . . I continue to fight dragons in the guise of insurance companies. Ignorance offends me, and I am doing what I need to do.

Asking for help has lent meaning to my suffering, as has accepting help. And now, in this precious bubble of health and energy where I live at the moment, helping gives tremendous meaning to my life. As a matter of fact, the minute I start helping, I am not suffering anymore.

What is suffering, anyhow? It is fallout from life moving on, as it naturally does. Suffering is an inextricable part of the beating heart of life. What is it the Buddhists say? Every life has ten thousand joys and ten thousand sorrows. If I aspire to avoid the sorrows, I will also avoid the joys. Life is short. I want it all.

What we think about our suffering is worse than the suffering itself. Suffering goes hand-in-hand with joy; you're not bad because you're suffering.

Epilogue

I have come to consider suffering as an opportunity.

The fact that health insurers have adopted a position of not paying is cruel and unfair; however, fighting them is your opportunity to find your power again. If they held the door for you, offered you a cup of latte, and paid for all of your treatments without question, you could easily languish in victim mode. A person could get used to all that care.

As it is, you have the fine opportunity to become empowered in the midst of your Serious Affliction. You have to, if you expect to survive it. The other day, one of my helpees said to me, "This is such a headache!" "WRONG," I said, "This is not a headache. This is your hero's journey. This is going to be the most worthwhile, best-paid work you will ever do. However, even better than that, you will know that you can bring a mighty bureaucracy to its knees. We cannot control the cancer; we can defeat those who would deny us treatment. This is your life. You need to get excited about it."

Do not expect your doctors to manage your case. Do not expect your doctors to know the safest and most effective treatment for your disease/condition. Become an "e-patient," make yourself an expert at Googling . . . until you know for sure that you have the most-qualified doctor in the world, and the most cutting-edge treatment for your condition. Then, take the bull by the horns, don't be afraid of anybody, never take "no" for an answer, and set off on your own hero's journey.

According to Angus Deacon, an economist at Princeton, the United States spends sixteen percent of its gross domestic product on healthcare, and it is almost impossible to know where the money goes. Let others address the issue of accountability in healthcare; I am here to make sure you get just enough of it to survive.

When you emerge from your time of Bad Medical Trouble, not only will you be in the best medical shape you can be, but you will be at peace, knowing that you did your utmost to save one precious life.

Glossary

As we already know, insurance words these days often mean the opposite of what they say. I offer my take on some common insurance terms:

Capitation

A system whereby the insurer pays a doctor or hospital a flat monthly fee for the care of each health plan member, whether or not any services are delivered. Shocking, isn't it? Say for example your Primary Care Physician (PCP) has one hundred patients, and he is allowed a thousand dollars a month to spend on each patient. What if you need six thousand dollars of care in one month, and he can't write it off against five patients who haven't been in this month? He is going to have to find a way to do some creative bookkeeping, or he is going to have to deny that care.

Co-insurance

Sounds pretty chummy, eh? Like a partnership . . . yes, I am pulling my own weight. WRONG. Co-insurance is the share of the covered charges—usually a percentage—that the insured and the plan each pay. Why is there always a percentage? BECAUSE THEY ALMOST NEVER PAY IT ALL. In many plans, even after you pay your deductible, you still have to shell out a percentage of the charges until your out-of-pocket limit is reached.

Co-Pay

The fixed dollar amount that the insured must pay at the time of service. Visit the doctor, pay a co-pay. Is it beginning to sound like, every time you turn around, YOU are paying, even though you supposedly have insurance coverage?

COBRA

A federal law that gives the right to workers to continue individual coverage for a specified period if the worker loses group coverage because of reduced work hours or because of losing his job. Individual coverage is scary-expensive . . . I would actively start looking for new group coverage as soon as I started on COBRA.

Coordination of Benefits (COB)

When the insured is covered by more than one plan, the benefits from all plans are coordinated so as not to pay more than 100% of the COVERED medical expenses—all of the expenses which the insurer deems "usual and customary." If you have more than one insurer, it is up to you to be an expert on ALL of them. If you think they won't make any mistakes while "coordinating" your benefits, you are wrong.

The purpose of COB is not to "work together," "coordinate your care," etc. It is to MAKE SURE THAT NO INSURANCE COMPANY PAYS MORE THAN IT HAS TO.

ERISA

Employee Retirement Income Security Act, a federal act that regulates employee-sponsored pension and insurance plans. The big healthcare providers must have lobbied hard for this law. It was enacted in 1974, several years after managed care came to be. Smell a cost containment rat here? On the face of it, ERISA protects your pension fund. (Which, is, of course, useless now that employers do not offer pensions anymore.) However, proceed to the health insurance part of the law. If you have your insurance as an employee, ERISA supersedes all state insurance laws, particularly in the area of "remedies" under the law. What does this mean to you? Hello, you cannot sue your health insurer for as much as you could if your state law were in charge . . . big sigh of relief for your health insurer.

Gatekeeper

The individual who controls access to services. Used to be the insurer, now it is your Primary Care Physician.

Experimental/Investigational procedures

Your health insurer often uses this phrase in order to deny care. They might say that the only effective treatment for your disease is "unproven, ineffective, or non-standard." They may resort to this objection after you have demolished all of their other objections.

These words are meant to make you give up. Press forward, knowing that they have not a shred of proof that your surgery/treatment is experimental. How could one prove such a thing? Besides, if your treatment were an "experiment" or a study, you would have by law to be notified of it.

Your insurer cannot prove that your treatment/surgery IS experimental, but you can easily prove that it IS NOT. Pile up mountains of proof about the thousands of people successfully treated with your proposed treatment, the published studies, papers, etc. Cite reputable sources such as the NIH, CDC, AMA, etc. who sanction your treatment of choice. Prove that, without your treatment of choice, you will suffer irreparable harm and probably die. It's easy, don't let this one stop you.

EOB

Explanation of Benefits . . . the insurer's explanation of what they have decided to pay on your claim. Read them, question them, do not hesitate to dispute them.

Grievance procedure

The required appeals process by which you the insured may protest a decision regarding a claim payment. Study it, follow it. When submitting any appeal by mail, be sure to send it Certified Mail (looks more serious that way) and write "expedited appeal" on your letter and on the envelope. No addressing your letter to "dear sir or madam." Call the insurer and get the correct name and title of the person to whom your appeal will be sent.

HIPAA

Healthcare Insurance Portability and Accountability Act. An amendment to ERISA which (supposedly) guarantees you healthcare coverage if you change jobs. This "group-to-group coverage" may be another illusion. If you have cancer treatment—and you change jobs—will HIPPA really guarantee that the new insurer will cover you? I doubt it. That new insurer will have plenty of fine print in place: waiting periods, pre-existing condition rules, etc. to keep you from your "guaranteed" continued coverage.

The one thing that HIPAA does for you, insurance-wise, is allow you to carry your coverage for eighteen months until you find a new job. This coverage is called COBRA. Big whoop-dee-doo, you will be PAYING THROUGH THE NOSE FOR IT. Hurry up and find a new job, and make sure that the new insurer is toeing the line with regard to the time limits on pre-existing conditions.

HIPPA also imposes strict privacy protections for our medical information. Sounds good, yes? I mean, you certainly don't want your employer sniffing around in your medical records. However, I would suggest that this provision also contains a very up-side for health insurers. They do not want patients to talk to each other. They don't want us to know what is going on big-picture. My oncologist told me how rare my cancer was, only ever seen two cases, etc., etc. Come to find out that there were at least ten HMO members at that time with the same disease. HIPPA makes it much easier for the insurer to divide and conquer, keeping us in the dark.

HMO

Health Maintenance Organizations. HMOs were the first invention of Managed Care, back in the early 1970s. They hire a group of doctors and nurses and put them in a facility. You join the HMO, and you have to go to a doctor within this "network" for your care. Unless, of course, you can prove that no doctor in the network is qualified to provide care for your disease/injury/condition.

Lifetime Maximum

The total dollar amount that your health plan will pay for your medical care.

You might want to check your own lifetime maximum . . . it is the most important number in your benefits booklet. Bear in mind that you can easily spend a million dollars in six months if you are in the hospital for an extended stay.

Managed Health Care Plans

A system that organizes and regulates doctors, hospitals and other providers in order to LOWER COSTS. This is the definition, people. Just so you know that the first priority of managed care—our modern healthcare system including HMOs, PPOs, POSs—is to pay less for your care.

Mandated Benefits

Healthcare benefits that state or federal law says must be included in healthcare plans. You might want to visit your local library and find out what these are.

Medically Necessary

A provision in a healthcare policy that excludes coverage for treatment that is not "medically necessary." Each insurer defines medical necessity differently. Sound like circular logic? It is. Just know that the fact that your insurer SAYS that your treatment is not "medically necessary" doesn't mean that you don't need it to maintain, preserve or restore your health. It just means that THEY DON'T WANT TO PAY FOR IT.

Network (In-network, Out-of-network)

All physicians, specialists, hospitals and other healthcare providers who agree to provide medical care to HMO/PPO members, under the terms of a contract. Generally speaking, HMOs only pay for services which are provided by doctors either in the network or contracted with the network. PPOs have an "out-of-network" benefit, which is 60%–80% of the "usual and customary" services. The purpose of this book is to help you find the most qualified doctor either in or out of your network, then make your insurer pay for your care.

Out-of-pocket limit

The dollar limit on the portion of covered medical expenses that the insured must pay during a benefit period (usually one year). When the out-of-pocket is met, the insured will not have to pay further deductibles or co-insurance until the next year. If you follow the tactics in this book, you may not even have to pay this. Along with everything else, I persuaded my insurer to pay my deductible AND my out-of-pocket during my year of Bad Medical Trouble.

Patient's Bill of Rights

If your insurer is denying, stonewalling, or otherwise opposing your best interests, step on over to the library and ask the reference librarian if your state has a Patient's Bill of Rights. The Patient's Bill of Rights is not a law, but it is a strong statement, often endorsed by legislators and certifying agencies, of what health insurers need to provide in terms of information, second opinions, appeals, etc.

POS (Point-of-service) plans

A POS is more of an "insurance product" than an organization. They may be offered by HMOs, PPOs, or employer-self-insured plans. These plans allow members the option of using services outside the network without prior approval. Sounds liberating, eh? Not so fast. The POS usually has a "financial disincentive" for going outside the network. What that means, in plain English, is that, if you go out of the network, they will pay a little and you will pay a lot.

Portability

Under HIPAA, workers with pre-existing medical conditions must receive credit for time in a previous health plan if they join a new employer's plan.

Pre-certification

You must seek approval from the insurer before you have surgery, check into the hospital, visit specialists, have expensive tests. This applies whether the specialists or services are in or out of the network. Also called "utilization review."

Pre-existing condition

A pre-existing condition is a health problem/condition/illness which you had prior to applying for insurance; and for which you received medical advice, diagnosis, care or treatment. Policies can exclude coverage of any medical condition for a period of time. If you have had Serious Medical Involvement, and you have to switch to a new insurer, you will want to scrutinize this part of the policy. Does it adhere to the HIPPA time limits for pre-existing conditions?

PPO (Preferred Provider Organization)

A network of doctors, hospitals, and suppliers (preferred providers) who agree to provide services to member of a health plan for reduced fees. One more way to cut costs. This PPO thing is troubling to me. How appealing really is an organization where everyone has to work cheap?

Premium

The amount you pay for your insurance. Your monthly bill for coverage.

Primary Care Physician

The physician selected by the insurance plan member who serves as a personal doctor and also functions as a gatekeeper for all costs and services. Sound like a conflict of interest? You bet.

Reasonable and customary fees (also known as "usual and customary")

When a bill for services is submitted, it is the insurer who gets to decide what is a "reasonable and customary" fee for those services. They decide this based on large computerized databases of information and sophisticated computer programs which are not available for review either by the provider or by the insured. In a word—secret.

Second Opinion

A second opinion is what you need to have if your doctor recommends surgery or a treatment with serious side effects. Usually, your benefits booklet will guarantee you the right to a second opinion. If the plan itself doesn't spell out its policy on second opinions, proceed on to your state's Patients' Bill of Rights or your state's Insurance Commissioner for legal back-up.

Don't be a chump and go for your second opinion to the doctor who is the partner of the guy who gave you the first opinion. If there is no doctor in the network qualified to give an opinion on treatment for your illness/injury/condition, you should be able to get your insurer to pay for the opinion out of network. If they won't pay, pay for the second opinion out of your own pocket. Your life could depend on it.

Third party administrator

They administer employee benefit plans under contract with insurance companies, HMOs and self-funded plans. If you are an employee, the third party administrator (or your Human Resources manager) may be the one who will help you in your quest to persuade the insurer to pay for your treatment.

Acknowledgments

Without Dr. Sugarbaker, there would be no book, because I would not be alive to write it. Thank you for dedicating your life to this rare cancer.

To the flock of angels who stood with me through it all: Hillary who took me to all Icky Doctor Appointments, Jens Laundrup who fought alongside me during my Insurance Wars, Dale who listened to me through the emotional wars, my mother who stood strong, Missy who fed me, and Linda who got on a plane to our nation's capital and brought me home . . . thank you.

To all of the friends and colleagues who, during my Year of Bad Medical Trouble, read my weekly reports. You prayed, sang, chanted, took me to the grocery store, and donated to the cause. For that I thank you.

To the Dorns. When I realized that I would have to go for major medical intervention in Washington, D.C., I remembered that Norman and Evelyn lived in the area. When I called, Norman did not hesitate, "We are making a room in our home, whatever you need, wherever you need to go." And so it came to pass, for my sister and I, for two months. To Norman and Evelyn and Nathan and Frederique . . . and Beth, who dropped everything, came to D.C., and took such tender care of me, I thank you.

And to the new ones, who have stood by me through the remaking of my life, PTSD and all: Gail who kept me closest and best company, Michael and Sandy who lifted me up and bailed me out, Barbara in New York who showed me how to do All This with style, Bob in Philadelphia who accepted me no matter what, and Robin in Phoenix, who touched my heart and changed me for the better. And the California Barbs—Barb in San Diego, who modeled humor in the face of Major Trouble, and Barb in Sonoma, who showed me what peace looks like.

Thank you also to Dr. Y., who showed me that—even at the HMO—one may find an accomplished, dedicated and thoughtful physician.

Finally, to all who made this a better book: Ilse, who gave so freely of her time, experience, and resources to bring this book to those who need it. Dr. Sticca, who helped me to curb my indignation and stay on message. Suzanne, who copy-edited with such skill and dedication. Desta, who went above and beyond to transform a manuscript into a real book. And Beth and David, who have understood and championed all of my projects. I thank you all.

With your help, it has been two very good years.

BOOK ORDER FORM

(please copy and fill out)

To order your copy of *Fight Your Health Insurer and Win: Secrets of the Insurance Warrior* by Laurie Todd, please provide the following information:

Name _____

Address _____

City _____ State ___ Zip ___

E-mail _____

Phone _____

Quantity_____ x $14.95: _____

SHIPPING & HANDLING: $5.00 for 1st book, $1.25 per book thereafter. Unless otherwise requested, books will be sent USPS media mail.

S & H: _____

Subtotal: _____

If ordering from Washington, please add 8.8% sales tax: _____

Order total: _____

Method of Payment: ☐ Check ☐ Money Order ☐ VISA

Credit Card # _____ Exp. Date # _____ ☐ MasterCard

Signature _____ ☐ American Express

Please copy this order form and send or fax with payment to:

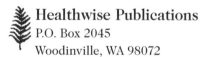

Healthwise Publications
P.O. Box 2045
Woodinville, WA 98072

Phone: 425-497-1858 / Fax: 425-820-5947
Email: laurie@theinsurancewarrior.com

Or order from our secure website:
www.theinsurancewarrior.com

Healthwise Publications may be purchased in bulk for education, business, or fundraising use. For information, please contact the publisher.